SLIM *from within*

DAVID BROOKES

FROM WITHIN LTD.

OTHER COURSES IN THIS SERIES:

BEAT STRESS FROM WITHIN
STOP SMOKING FROM WITHIN

OTHER BOOKS BY THE SAME AUTHOR

BREATHE STRESS AWAY

Details of how to obtain these can be found at the back of this book.

Contents

Copyright © 1997 David Brookes

ISBN 0-9527105-4-4

Sixth Reprint 2000

FROM WITHIN LTD
PO BOX 146
SHREWSBURY
SHROPSHIRE SY3 8WA

Printed and bound in The United Kingdom
by Page Bros of Norwich
Set in Times

For Siv and Heidi

My thanks, firstly to Peter Phillips, whose enthusiasm, support and vision have done so much to bring the seeds of this project to fruition.
My thanks to Bill for helping me to see the love in others and holding the mirror when I needed it. To Kaska for drawing out of me what I was looking for. To Tony, Rob and Stephan for their encouragement and help along the way. To Georgie for her illustrations. To Mandy, Terry and Paul, whose teaching opened the door and to Paul McKenna who shone a light on the pathway.

My special thanks to my hundreds of clients, from whom I have learned so much over the years.

Illustrations by Georgie Cowan

Using this Slim From Within book is very simple.

Work at your own pace.
If you do not work with the course for a few days do a quick recap up to the point that you have reached.

Most people wishing to lose weight are looking for a quick fix.
There is no such thing.
The more you chase it the more disappointed you will be.

DO NOT BE TEMPTED TO RUSH.

IF YOU RUSH YOU WILL ACHIEVE LESS.

YOU HAVE SPENT YEARS GETTING TO WHERE YOU ARE NOW SO IT WILL TAKE SOME TIME TO MAKE ALL THE CHANGES THAT YOU NEED TO.

This book is not something to be read just once and then put away.
It is something to work with.

Many chapters have exercises for you to do.
If you are to benefit fully from the course, it is absolutely essential that you do them all.
The one you decide to skip over may hold the very key to permanent weight loss that you are looking for!
There is no substitute for doing the exercises. Skipping over them with a vague intention of coming back to them later will not work.
Equip yourself with your own notebook to accompany the course so that you can keep all your notes and learning in one place.

Share what you learn with others.
It helps to reinforce your own learning.
The more people you share it with the better your own learning.
Two of you may wish to use the book together. Exchanging ideas and giving each other support as you go along can be a very effective.

Each time you finish a Slim From Within session, arrange a time with yourself when you will continue.

Commitment, self-responsibility and persistence will become familiar words to you as you work through the course.
You can carry the weight of them on your shoulders or you can have them as your friends.
As friends they will bring you energy, enthusiasm and success.
The choice is yours.

Choose wisely.

INTRODUCTION

LIGHTEN UP!

Welcome to the wonderful world of weight loss.

For most people it is a world full of conflict, disappointment and frustration, so how can it be wonderful?

Well, not only can it be wonderful, it can also be pleasurable, exciting and fulfilling.

Now, this idea may seem very strange to many of you reading this book. You will probably be thinking weight loss is all about dieting, willpower and denial.

How can that possibly be enjoyable?

When you listen to people who have achieved permanent weight loss they all say very similiar things:

- *Life is great*
- *I feel like a new person*
- *I look at life differently now*
- *I wake up looking forward to each day*
- *I never realised how much I was missing*

If losing weight is so awful, how can it bring so much pleasure and reward?

It is obvious that when people lose weight permanently something else happens apart from just losing weight.

Exactly what this is intrigued me, so I decided to research in detail the case histories of my clients over the years to see if I could discover what happened differently for those people who not only lost weight but kept it off permanently.

And then something remarkable happened. I discovered a pattern.

From this I have developed the *Slim From Within* approach to weight loss. I hope you will benefit from it, as thousands have.

1.
SETTING OUT

Losing weight is a little bit like setting out on a boat journey. You know where you want to go and somebody has told you what course to steer. Unfortunately, they don't really know you or where you are starting your journey from. You only need to start one degree off course and by the end of a week you are heading miles in the wrong direction.

If you start from the wrong place you end up in the wrong place – either not losing weight at all or if losing it almost certainly putting it back on.

People who lose weight effectively and permanently start from a different place from those who put it back on. They have a different view of weight loss, they see things differently.

Slim From Within is aimed at putting you in the right place to start from and providing you with an understandable map to help you find your way forward.

Most people reading this book will have lost weight at some time in their lives, and the likelihood is that they will have put it back on again. That is because they have dieted, and that is what dieting does. Most diets provide a temporary, unnatural relationship with food which is often unhealthy, usually unrealistic and when it is the only strategy for change, never results in permanent weight loss.

Most dieters are very confused as to what is going on. They have no conscious awareness of the processes that have established their relationship with food, or how these influence them throughout the course of a day.

This confusion is not surprising when there are so many books and so much information on weight loss now available. Even if an individual has found a strategy which actually works for them in some way, the power of advertising often pulls them in a new direction.

If we do not clearly understand our relationship with food — what purpose we are using it for besides providing energy for our body and mind — then we will never be able to change that relationship.

The mind and body can become a battleground of fear, failure, self-doubt, anger, self-criticism and judgement. Whilst the confusion continues, so will the battle.

If you start from the right place your chances of finding permanent weight loss are greatly increased.

Weight loss is a little bit like a jigsaw puzzle, all the pieces need to fit together if we are to get the complete picture. It is very difficult to put together a jigsaw puzzle if you do not have a picture on the front of the box.

Slim From Within is about seeing the whole picture. A unique picture of yourself as you are now and of how you wish to be in the future. It provides the framework for you to create that future reality. Even as you are reading this your imagination can begin to create that future picture of yourself – of how you are going to look with all your weight loss worries behind you.

Dieting simply cannot be the whole answer or everybody who had ever been on a diet would be slim!

So what are the pieces of this jigsaw puzzle?

How do they fit together?
Where can you buy them?
Do they come in milkshakes or bars?
What flavours do they come in ?
How much do they cost?
Is there some magic ingredient ?

Not at all.

They are things we all have but often fail to recognise.

They are the unconscious processes:

Our belief system.
Our thoughts.
Our emotions.
Our behaviour.

They combine to create each of us as unique individuals. Our bodies are a physical reflection of the state of these internal processes.

They all have a deep and profound effect on our body and they determine our relationship with food.

A change in them is absolutely vital to achieve pleasurable and permanent weight loss.

As you move through this book you will become aware of them, how they have been influencing how you eat, and how they can be changed to work <u>for</u> you rather than <u>against</u> you.

THE MENTAL ICEBERG

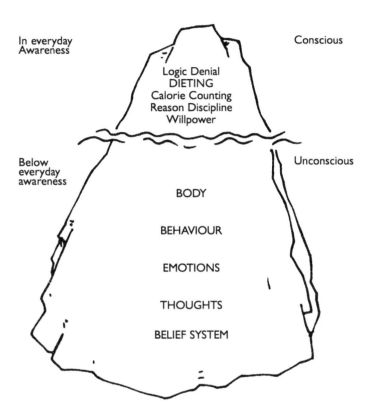

In everyday
Awareness

Conscious

Logic Denial
DIETING
Calorie Counting
Reason Discipline
Willpower

Below
everyday
awareness

Unconscious

BODY

BEHAVIOUR

EMOTIONS

THOUGHTS

BELIEF SYSTEM

HOW OUR UNCONSCIOUS PROCESSES AFFECT WEIGHT LOSS

The majority of causes for over-eating lie at the unconscious level. By unconscious, I mean those internal processes of which we are unaware most of the time, but which greatly influence the part food plays in our lives.

We sometimes open the fridge door when we are not hungry, we nibble away in the evening watching television often without even being aware that we are eating.

Sometimes we might start eating and find that we cannot stop. These and similiar such habits all have their origins below our level of conscious awareness.

When we try to make changes at a conscious level, as most dieters do, we are really only dealing with the tip of the iceberg.

As with an iceberg, so it is with the cause of overeating: 90 per cent of it is below the surface.

When the real issues are tackled, weight drops off with hardly any conscious effort to change eating habits. New habits often develop quite naturally at an unconscious level and we find ourselves losing weight.

BELIEF SYSTEM

Our bodies do the best they can to agree with our belief system. If the way we treat our bodies, for example by dieting, is in conflict with our inner beliefs then we enter a battleground of conflicting ideas. For instance, if one of your beliefs is; *I am not successful at anything*, then that is the reality your body will agree with and try to create. It will not allow you to be successful at dieting no matter how many times you try. Identifying and changing these central beliefs is essential to permanent weight loss. There are a whole range of these self-limiting beliefs. Before we can begin to change them we must identify them.

THOUGHTS

Our thoughts are a reflection of our beliefs. We are often our own worst inner critics. Most of us would not dream of speaking to other people the way we criticise ourselves. When we find ourselves not sticking to a diet, for example, we might say *I am so useless, I have failed again, I will never be able to lose weight.* So our thoughts are reflecting our belief that we will not be successful. We have control over our thoughts and we can change them so that they help us rather than work against us.

EMOTIONS

Emotions are a physical response to our thoughts.

There are a number of opinions about how many emotions we experience. Most people would agree that those we are most familiar with are anger, joy, sadness and fear. Cultural, social, family and relationship pressures often create an emotional imbalance within us. We are very good at expressing some emotions but there are some we may not be so comfortable with. The way we feel is a direct reflection of what we believe and what we think. Food is one of the most common ways of attempting to deal with emotions which remain unexpressed. Again, only when we can identify our own emotional food connection, can we set about changing it.

BEHAVIOUR

The behaviour we are concerned with here is that of eating when we are not hungry or sometimes not being able to stop eating once we have started. Dieting is an attempt to change that behaviour at a conscious level with willpower and discipline. It is not the most effective way to start losing weight. We need to look first at the unconscious processes. Once they are in agreement that over-eating is no longer useful or desirable then we are in the right place to go forward and begin to establish a new healthy eating lifestyle.

OUR BODY

Our body is a reflection of our internal and unconscious processes. It has its own intelligence and knowledge and is able to hold on to emotions and to support our beliefs and thoughts. If there is an imbalance somewhere on the inside, then that will be reflected somewhere in the body. Over-eating is an attempt to find that inner balance, but all it does is to reflect it and cause a physical imbalance.

These processes are constantly at work within us, without us even being aware that they are there. There was probably a time when you had a battle with yourself over a particular food. You knew how many calories it contained, you knew it was not healthy food, you knew you would feel guilty afterwards – and yet your hand picked it up and you ate it.

Why did you do that?

Why did you feel guilty afterwards?

Why does every diet you have tried feel like a battlefield of inner conflict?

What is this unwanted behaviour of over-eating really about?

Well, the issue we are really attempting to deal with through food is probably not even being acknowledged at a conscious level, let alone recognised.

All these processes work together and they interact and combine to make us the unique individuals that we are. As we change any one of them, there is a ripple effect through every part of us. For instance, if we change a belief from: *I have tried to lose weight and failed so I will probably fail next time,* to: *I can successfully lose weight*, then that has a tremendously powerful effect on how we think, feel and behave.

One of the absolutely essential elements of the *Slim From Within* approach to weight loss is the order in which you look at and move through these unconscious processes.

The four steps to permanent weight loss:

From BELIEFS to THOUGHTS to EMOTIONS to BEHAVIOUR.

If you try to think yourself slim without believing it is possible for you to succeed, you will always sabotage your efforts.

If you try to let go of the weight of unexpressed emotions without changing your thoughts, you will never succeed, for your emotions come from your thoughts.

If you try and change your pattern of over-eating, whilst you do not have a different way of coping with your emotions, any change will only be temporary.

ONCE WE HAVE ACHIEVED A CHANGE AND BALANCE WITHIN OURSELVES THEN WE CAN EXPECT TO ACHIEVE A CHANGE AND HAPPY BALANCE ON THE SCALES.

2.
FINDING YOUR FEET

**WHAT YOU CAN DO,
OR DREAM YOU CAN DO, BEGIN IT;
BOLDNESS HAS GENIUS,
POWER AND MAGIC IN IT.**
(Goethe)

Before you can lose weight permanently the foundations need to be in place and you take the steps forward there are certain aspects of the process of which you must be aware of these from the outset. It is important that you carry this knowledge and awareness with you.

SELF-RESPONSIBILITY

It is you who are overweight.

Nobody has forced you to eat what you have eaten. You have chosen to eat the foods that you have eaten. Now is your opportunity to choose otherwise.

If you are blaming others for your weight, you will never be free to change things because you are handing the responsibility to somebody else.

The more responsibility you take for your body, the greater power and strength you will have to change it.

A book, or a healthy eating plan means nothing unless you take the responsibility of using it to achieve what you want to achieve.

At this stage you just have to agree with one statement, and if you can accept this, then sign below and move on.

I AM RESPONSIBLE FOR WHAT I EAT

Signed _____

HOW YOU-YOU BECOMES YO-YO

There is an old saying:
The more you do of what you are doing,
The more you get of what you are getting.

This is especially true with regard to attempts at losing weight.
We have come to expect that for any weight loss approach to be successful, weight loss should be immediate. That is what we are attracted to – the idea of a quick easy diet.
Unless conditions are right within us – emotional and psychological – we will experience this expectation many times and each time it will fail. Our weight will increase and we will begin to yo-yo diet.
The term yo-yo dieting is quite apt when applied to the body, as the body does indeed go up and down in weight. But a body only does what a mind tells it. So what is happening to a mind to cause this process? The fact is that no real changes are taking place, the mind is just putting itself and the body through a process of denial.
If I were to say to you now: *Close your eyes for a moment and <u>don't</u> think of an ice cream,* you would instantly think of ice cream. That is a natural human reaction, which when applied to food puts us straight into a situation of denial — a world of *you shoulds* and *you should nots*. We hear so often, "to lose weight *you should* do this, *you should not* think that, *you should not* eat certain foods". The more we listen to

and try to follow this you-you approach to weight loss the more likely we are to fall into the yo-yo pattern. It is only when you-you changes to I-I and we begin to take responsibility for caring for our bodies with a permanent healthy eating plan that weight loss can truly become a pleasure. We can really enjoy watching our body respond to the care we give it.

We use willpower and other conscious thought processes in the hope of achieving and maintaining weight loss. But it never happens, because we hold on to two conflicting thoughts: *I want something* and *I should not have it.* Eventually a want will always overcome a should in relation to food. However, if we let go of the should, and the want is a want for healthy food then weight loss will be a result of mind and body having a common goal.

Dieting is an attempt to re-balance ourselves physically, but if we do not balance what lies on the inside, we cannot hope to balance what we see on the outside.

COMMITMENT

How committed are you to losing weight?
This time, are you willing to do what it takes?

This time it can be different.

You will achieve less by rushing.
You can work at your own pace.
You run a serious risk of success.
You do need persistence.

Can you read the following out loud and really mean it?
If so, sign below.

I am committed to losing weight permanently.
I am committed to looking at myself.
I am committed to being honest with myself.

Signed _____

**IF THERE IS NO COMMITMENT
THERE IS NO INVOLVEMENT.
IF THERE IS NO INVOLVEMENT
THERE IS NO RESULT.**

WILLPOWER VERSUS IMAGINATION

Most dieters use some form of willpower to lose weight. Willpower is something that you have to carry around with you for every waking moment if it is to have any chance of working. Unfortunately, we are human and this is not always possible. Willpower is a conscious process. But most causes for over-eating lie at the unconscious level. If we are using willpower to lose weight and we have not dealt with these underlying causes for over-eating, as soon as we stop using our willpower for a moment the old eating habits leap back in and take over. We then feel as though we have failed. Dieters usually recover from this failure and set themselves up for the whole cycle again.
So what can we learn from this?
That willpower as a sole strategy for comfortable and permanent weight loss does not work.
It can be a useful resource to draw on at times, but if we try to use it as the only approach we will fail. The use of willpower only denies us of something pleasurable. When something occurs to knock us off balance in life the old familiar triggers will be pressed and old eating habits return. Willpower can be useful in changing some behaviours, when an unwanted habit can be stopped completely, such as smoking or nail biting. With eating, however, it is different. We cannot stop completely or we'd die. If we try to lose weight using willpower alone, each day becomes a succession of temptations and decisions. *Shall I or shan't I eat this or that?* It can be time consuming and exhausting.
The good news is that you do not need much willpower to lose weight permanently. Even better news is that you have something far more powerful, that you have probably never used for weight loss, your imagination. The power of the imagination is phenomenal, and when used to help us achieve permanent weightloss, is far stronger than willpower.
Take a few moments to see if you can use willpower to create goose bumps on your arm. When you have finished, close your eyes, take a deep breath and imagine that a cool breeze is blowing over your arm. If you stay with that thought long enough goose bumps will indeed appear. Do not worry if you cannot create this immediately at this

stage. As with muscles, the imagination needs exercise and gets stronger with use.

As you progress through this book, the various exercises will give you the opportunity to unlearn old, unwanted habits and to create your own reality by using the wonderful power of your imagination.

Imagine how you wish your body to be. That is the reality you can now begin to create.

FROM CONSCIOUS TO UNCONSCIOUS

There is a process of learning which takes us from conscious incompetence to unconscious competence. In other words, thinking we cannot do something, learning how to do it, and then doing it without even thinking about it. When this happens the learning produces virtually automatic behaviour. Driving a car, for instance. We initially learn how to operate each piece of equipment separately. After some time the use of indicators, gears, clutch and brake all become coordinated and we are able to drive automatically. We have then become unconsciously competent.

Imagine going into a supermarket for the first time; you have to search for each individual item on the shelves. After a few visits you begin to learn where everything is and you can actually shop more quickly whilst thinking of many other things at the same time. The learned process goes into the long-term memory store below your level of conscious awareness.

Although it is not a skill we would choose to acquire, the same process happens with over-eating. We find ourselves doing it automatically, sometimes starting to eat without even noticing that we are eating at all. This frequently occurs when we use food for some other purpose than just to satisfy our hunger. For instance, in the misguided belief that it will give us a feeling of comfort. The over-eating becomes automatic and we come to see it as just a habit. We then seek to change the habit whilst ignoring the real issue: we're searching for comfort in our lives.

There are other issues, apart from the need for comfort, which cause us to over-eat. They are usually stored in our unconscious mind, below our everyday level of awareness. As you move through this book, you will have the excitement of discovering them and the real pleasure of letting them go.

Over-eating is an attempt to deal with an emotional state which is usually below our level of everyday awareness.

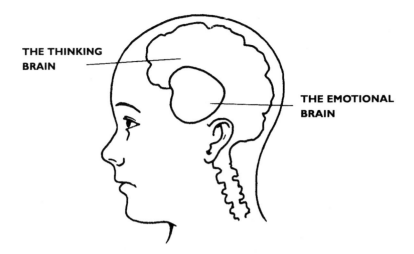

THE THINKING BRAIN

THE EMOTIONAL BRAIN

LEARNING - *that's something we used to do at school, isn't it?*

Well, yes it is. There is, however, a continual process of learning going on for us every moment of our lives. Some might argue that we cannot learn whilst we are asleep but many a problem has been solved by *sleeping on it.*

The brain has various parts which have different functions. With regard to weight loss there are two parts of which it is particularly useful to be aware.

Firstly, there is the THINKING BRAIN, or the neo-cortex, as it is called by scientists. Most approaches to weight loss address this part of the brain. We COUNT calories, we REASON which foods are the right ones, we UNDERSTAND how a particular diet is based on sound LOGIC.

There is, however, another part of the brain which is crucial to effective and permanent weight loss, and this is the EMOTIONAL BRAIN. Many approaches to weight loss fail to address this area at all and yet it is essential that we do so. Not only is it the centre of our emotions but it also deals with our feeling of hunger, our metabolic rate and the production of hormones.

The emotional associations we have with food originate here. If we ignore the emotion-food connection, and approach weight loss with only the thinking brain, then nothing really changes. We only deal with the tip of the iceberg. We are missing vital pieces of the jigsaw puzzle. The emotional brain has a very strong link with our long-term memory. We remember events that have a high emotional content very well. If you take a few moments to recall something you remember well — it

might be a wedding, a holiday, a love-affair or whatever you choose —
you will notice that it has a strong emotional content. Our earliest
associations with food also have a high emotional content. We only
have to be aware of the noisy and tearful distress of a hungry baby
which changes to smiles and gurgles of contentment once fed.

During the process of changing your relationship with food you will
find yourself being in touch with new sources of contentment and
pleasure, but without having to have food as their source.

**When people lose weight and keep it off there is always a change
in feeling. If there is no change in feeling there is no permanent
change in weight.**

UNLEARNING

Unlearning is probably the most important process in changing our
relationship with food. We need to unlearn the belief that food can be
used as a substitute for something other than hunger. We need to
acknowledge the emotional state which has an association with food,
and to unlearn the food/emotion association. We have to find realistic
and better ways of handling that emotion, and to learn that overeating
doesn't help. We need to change our relationship with food.

Many relationships run into problems because of unrealistic
expectations of a partner – we want them to be a parent as well as a
lover. We want them to give what our parents never provided, which is
not only unrealistic but often unfair.

In a similiar way we have unrealistic expectations of our relationship
with food. We believe, unconsciously, that it will change our emotional
state, that it will make us feel better.

As we prepare to lose weight it is as if we have to divorce food, to let
go of the old relationship and start a new one. We enter this new
relationship as an adult rather than as a child and the balance of the
relationship is just how we choose it to be.

When this happens we relate to food differently, and it begins to play
a different role in our lives.

We must unlearn our current relationship with food in the same way
we first learnt it.

Attempts just to change the amount and type of food will have no
permanent effect. Our body is a physical representation of our beliefs,
thoughts, emotions and behaviour. When the unlearning is complete, a
new healthy relationship with food is established, and our body is free
to find its best weight.

**It is what we need to unlearn about our relationship with food that
leads to permanent weight loss.**

LAPSE LEARNING

Lapse learning is a phrase that can be given to what are usually called mistakes, or what the dieter very often calls failures.

Lapses are an excellent opportunity to learn. They show us that we need to do something differently. If we consistently make the same mistake, we only need to find one new piece of learning to put ourselves back in the right direction.

When an automatic pilot is used to steer a course on a boat, weather conditions, winds, tides and currents all change and the boat moves off-course. But because the automatic pilot knows where it is going, it constantly makes adjustments, so that the boat will arrive at the right place. Despite the boat moving in the wrong direction, it is never off course for very long.

So it can be with lapses. We know we are going in the wrong direction as soon as it happens, so we make an adjustment.

The difference between ourselves and automatic pilots is that if we are vigilant, responsible, and committed enough, we can learn not to make the same error again.

We so often attack and criticise ourselves for making a mistake instead of asking the question: *What do I need to learn here?*

Begin now and practise using this question.

If we learned from every lapse we made, we would all be slim by now!

WHY ARE YOU HOLDING ON TO YOUR WEIGHT?

We sometimes have a reason, below our level of awareness, that makes us want to hold on to our weight.

In the world of psychology this is called a *secondary gain* and can take many different forms. One way of identifiying this *secondary gain* is to ask yourself: *What does keeping weight bring me? What purpose does it serve?*

For some people keeping the weight can make them appear to be bigger, stronger than others. Size can be intimidating. It can create an illusion of strength. If a person has low self-esteem and feels small and weak on the inside, then physical size can be used as a compensation for this.

Keeping weight on is sometimes used to keep yourself unattractive to the opposite sex. If you have been in a relationship that involved a lot of pain, then staying fat can be a way of keeping the opposite sex away, and of stopping a new relationship developing.

If someone was unfaithful in their relationship in the past, then making themselves unattractive can be used as a way of preserving their current relationship.

Struggling to lose weight can bring sympathy and attention from partners, family and others. Any sort of attention is better than no attention at all.

Being overweight can be an excuse for not taking part in activities that we do not feel self-confident about, such as swimming, dancing, mixing with people socially, taking part in sports. If we cannot physically do these, we are unlikely to be pressurised by others.

Some people become socially dependent on the struggle to lose weight and the contact it brings with other individuals or groups.

All such secondary gains operate below the level of everyday awareness. The common element is that they all operate as some form of control over others. We usually need to operate control when we have fear.

Look closely at what you have to gain by not losing weight.
It may hold the key to setting yourself free.

WHY DO YOU WANT TO LOSE WEIGHT?

There are some reasons which are very useful in helping us lose weight permanently.

There are also others which are not so useful.

Not useful:

Losing weight for other people: eg. partner, parents, friends, to impress social circle.
Such reasons just let us know that we value other people's opinions above our own. We wish to please others and we are hungry for approval and acceptance.

To look like people in the public eye
To be fashionable
To fit in with advertising images

Such reasons cut us off from our own individuality and sense of worth.

They set unrealistic expectations which undermine confidence and self-esteem.
Trying to meet such expectations can be extremely harmful to body and mind.

Partly useful reasons:

To feel better
To find a partner
To like what I see in the mirror
To get rid of my depression

Such reasons are useful in so much as they give us a clear clue to the issues which underly our over-eating habits.

The above answers should help us ask the following questions:

Why do I not feel good?
What am I lacking in my life that I believe a partner will bring?
Who has told me I am not good enough as I am?
Why am I depressed and what can I do to change it?

Losing weight will not help resolve these issues.
Resolving these issues will help you lose weight.

> **IT IS ONLY BY LOOKING AT WHAT WE
> EXPECT WEIGHT LOSS WILL GIVE US,
> AND THEN RECOGNISING THAT IT WON'T,
> THAT WE BECOME TRULY FREE TO SET UP
> A NEW RELATIONSHIP WITH FOOD.**

Reasons which greatly enhance the chances of permanent weight loss:

I care about my body
I care about myself
I care about my health
I enjoy living and want to be here as long as I can

Such reasons come from within us.
They are not just reactions to what is happening in our relationships or the world around us.
They are long term.
They are based on self-responsibilty and love.

Write your reasons for wanting to lose weight:

THE DECISION

Have you **decided** to lose weight permanently?
Or are you just thinking about it?

Is it something that you **really want** to happen?
Or is it just something you would like to happen?

Are you going to **make it happen**?
Or are you just going to hope it happens?

Do you want **long-term results**?
Or are you content with repeated short-term fixes?

Are you prepared to **learn new ways**?
Or do you want to repeat old habits?

Have you decided to **do whatever it takes**?
Or are you just going to give it a go?

Are you focused on a **positive end result**?
Or are you thinking of difficulties on the way?

Have you decided to **take action**?
Or are you just going to react to circumstances?

When you have made the decision to lose weight permanently you will notice your energy changing.
You will know what direction you are going in.
Making a decision gives you the freedom to achieve.
It gives you a sense of direction, momentum and focus.

Anything stopping you making a decision is a self-limiting belief.
Make a note of it; you will soon have the opportunity to let go of it.

You can make the decision now to lose weight permanently or you can make it when you choose.
But if you are going to be successful you will have to make it.
If you do not make the decision you do not have anywhere to start from.
If you do not have anywhere to start from you have nowhere to go to.

This book can be of no use unless you decide to use it.

I HAVE DECIDED TO LOSE WEIGHT PERMANENTLY.

Signed ————————————————————————

SO, TO SUMMARIZE THESE FIRST STEPS ON YOUR JOURNEY TO PERMANENT WEIGHT LOSS:

(Read these out loud to yourself)

I can enjoy the process of losing weight.

When I lose weight permanently, something else will happen apart from just losing weight.

When I start from the right place my chances of permanent weight loss are far greater.

Dieting is an attempt to rebalance myself physically, but if I do not balance what lies on the inside I cannot hope to balance what I see on the outside.

My unconscious processes determine my relationship with food. A change in them is vital to achieve pleasurable and permanent weight loss.
I can imagine how I want my body to be, and that is the reality I am beginning to create.

It is what I unlearn about my current relationship with food that will lead to permanent weight loss.

When I lose weight and keep it off there will be a change in how I feel. If there is no change in feeling there is no permanent weight loss.

My body is a physical representation of my belief system, thoughts, emotions and behaviour. Now I am establishing a new relationship with food, the balance on the inside will be reflected on the outside.

I am responsible for my weight.

I am committed to change.

I have decided to lose weight permanently

Always remember that your new relationship with food will be enjoyable. You are letting go of the old habits of eating the wrong foods for the wrong reasons, at the wrong times and in the wrong quantities. But you can still enjoy the thought of dinner parties, barbecues, and the pleasure and fun of eating together in good company. All these are vital and healthy parts of your new relationship with food.
Food can become a friend whose company you enjoy when you choose to, rather than an enemy with whom you are constantly battling.

You do not need to feel deprived or starved. You are actually becoming involved in a new relationship which can be as positive, enjoyable and vital as you choose to make it!

**WEIGHT LOSS WITH PAIN
OR WEIGHT LOSS WITH PLEASURE,
THE CHOICE IS YOURS**

3.
SHAPING YOUR CHANGE

THE RISKS OF CHANGE

I will like myself,
I will begin to enjoy each moment,
I will be able to enjoy the happiness of others,
I will smile at myself each morning,
I will start to see opportunities rather then problems,
I will enjoy what I have, rather than dwell on what I have not,
I will be responsible for my own happiness,
I will learn that when I carry fear, I will condemn others,
I will notice that when I give love, I forgive,
I will learn the joy of receiving as well as giving,
I will experience letting go of the past, the freedom of the present,
and welcoming the future.

THE RISKS OF NO CHANGE

I will stay the same

Most of us do not like change. We find change scarey. Remember your first day at school? The discomfort of staying where we are in life is often preferable to going through changes. But like it or not, we are continually going through changes in our lives. We leave home, we go to work, we enter new relationships and finish old ones, we become parents and we change our values and ambitions.

Change is a little bit like buying a new pair of shoes. They look great in the shop window and they feel really good the first time we try them on. However, the first time we wear them for a whole day they do not seem so comfortable. It is really good to come home and take them off and put the old ones back on again. Over a period of time we wear them a little bit more often, until we break them in. We become used to them and they feel so comfortable we do not wear the old ones any more. So it is with change. We are attracted to the idea but it takes a little while to get used to it.

Change is a very necessary and healthy process in life. For most people it also brings a certain amount of anxiety. It need not be that way. As you are ending your current relationship with food and starting a new one so you will go through a process of change. To recognise where you are in the process can make it a lot less stressful.

There are several stages in the process of change. As you become aware of them you will begin to notice where you ran into difficulties in the past, where your motivation and the momentum of your attempts at weight loss faltered. It is reassuring to see just where you are in that process and how important it is that you continue to go forward if you really want to change.

BEING STUCK

When this first stage occurs we may not like how we feel or how we look. We cannot see a way forward. This stage feels more intense if we have tried and failed to lose weight in the past and expect to fail again. Our inner voice replays negative messages:

I do not have enough willpower,
No diet works for me,
I will always fail at losing weight.

If, however, the expectation is positive and we become aware that there is a way forward, then we do not feel so intensely stuck.

You are soon going to find yourself in the right place and state to lose weight. Keep hold of that expectation – it will be very useful.

DENIAL

Denial is a very normal and necessary reaction when confronted with the idea that we should make a change. We tend to become very defensive about ourselves. Some people deny the need for change completely and blame others for their situation. This is because they fear change. Some people's reactions at this stage may sound familiar.

I do not see why I should lose weight anyway, it is okay to be fat.
How could my feelings have anything to do with what I eat?
What do you mean I have put on weight? Of course I haven't.

We also search around for reassurance from others to confirm our attempts at denial.

I look alright, don't I?
We all eat the wrong foods at times, don't we?
Shall we eat this together? (If I do it with someone else I will only feel half as bad).

Denial is okay, it gives us time to pull together our resources to move along through the process of change. But if you stay in denial your weight stays with you.

ANGER

There are many causes for anger, which you will have the chance to look at in more detail later. There is also an energy in anger. It is usually the energy of blame.

What right have they got to criticise me?
My parents taught me to love food, I am fat because of them.
Why do people think slim is beautiful?
How dare you suggest I am dealing with anger through food,
I DON'T GET ANGRY!
Of course I over-eat, wouldn't you if you were in this marriage?

Anger is also sometimes associated with the fact that if you are going to change how you feel and how you eat, the responsibility lies with you, and you do not want it!

DEPRESSION

It may come as a surprise to some people that depression is an essential and healthy part of the change process. Denying and avoiding change and staying angry are not comfortable places to be. As we become aware that maybe people are right in what they are saying, and we must make changes, we become depressed. Depression sometimes feels like our life is out of control and that we have no power to change. People may say:

My eating is out of control, I cannot do anything about it.
I am depressed because I am eating and I am eating because
I am depressed.

In this situation, changes have to be made. Once individuals realise that they are already in the process of change, things seem much easier. Both depression and over-eating are telling us it is time for a change.

LETTING GO

Until you reach this stage you are still attached to your old behaviours and thoughts. You have been hanging on to your old relationship with food. It is at this stage that you step into the present, into reality. There comes the realisation that as long as you hold on to your old beliefs, thoughts, feelings and behaviours you will not feel good, and so you let them go.
Once this takes place, the positive feelings from the process of change can be felt. You sense a growing optimism, a release, a lightness. You become more active and often reconnect with your sense of humour.

ACCEPTANCE

This brings a gradual feeling of comfort. The new shoes have been broken in and you discover that they are comfortable to wear. There is a time of adjustment as you adapt to your new lifestyle. You grow into a new way of relating to yourself, to others and to food.
After a burst of activity in getting used to how the "new me" behaves, the changes are absorbed and consolidated at every level within you. You emerge CHANGED and with a new relationship with food.

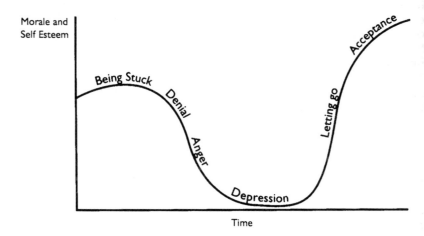

Time

RECOGNISING YOUR CHANGE

Each person's experience of change is unique. Many would-be dieters stay locked in denial, anger and depression. Seldom do we ever move smoothly from one stage to another. Some never get beyond the dip in feeling that is at the centre of change, but just keep on repeating the process in the form of yo-yo dieting. Some people move through it very rapidly. There is no right or wrong way but movement is essential.

There is often a stage of breakthrough, an *Aha!* as people realise that they are letting go. This may bring tears, but they rapidly move from tears of sadness to tears of joy at the release it brings.

There is always a gift waiting to be unwrapped in the process of change. It is a wonderful feeling of enlightenment when we see the present staring us in the face.

KNOWING WHERE I AM IN THE PROCESS OF CHANGE

Many people in today's society have lost touch with their feelings; they are often emotionally immobilised. Being in touch with your gut-feeling is the best barometer you have. Self-esteem, motivation and momentum all vary throughout the process of change. You are your own best judge as to where you are at any one time. If you check out how positive and confident you feel, it will give a good indication of just where you are.
You will be given ways to support and deal with the changes you are making in your relationship with food as you move through the book. Here are a few strategies to help you on your way:

Describe to yourself the change that you want, and check which stage you are at.

If possible communicate with others going through the same change.

Picture how you will be when the change has been achieved, and the positive feelings that will come with it.

Acknowledge what you did in the past to lose weight, see where it failed, and learn from this.

Focus on what you want, not on what you do not want.
If you feel stuck, remember that this is just a resting place on your journey.
You can and will go forward when you choose to.
Standing still is far more painful than changing.
Change involves a letting go of part of the past, acknowledging the needs of the present and creating the future you choose.

YOU WILL KNOW YOU HAVE CHANGED
WHEN NORMAL FEELS DIFFERENT.

4.
STEP ONE:
YOUR BELIEF SYSTEM

**YOU ARE WHAT YOU BELIEVE YOU ARE.
YOU CAN BECOME WHAT YOU BELIEVE
YOU CAN BECOME.**

AS LONG AS I DEFEND MY LIMITATIONS
SO WILL I KEEP THEM

WHAT IS A BELIEF SYSTEM?

Your belief system is the window through which you see the world. It determines what you see and how you react to it. It determines whether your pathway to permanent weight loss is going to be successful or not.

Beliefs are a set of deeply held inner guiding principles which we have each created, and which we constantly reinforce with every experience we have in life.

Sometimes our beliefs create self-defeating behaviours, constant frustration and unhappiness. On the other hand, our beliefs can create success, joy and a body we are really happy with.

The choice is ours.

Do you choose to see a glass half-full or half-empty?

Do you feel the rain on your face and enjoy being outdoors watching nature renew itself, or do you see the grey clouds above?

Your beliefs determine your inner response to the outside world. It does not matter if these beliefs are based on logic and rationality or fantasy and illusion, your unconscious will always attempt to support these beliefs. When an acceptable idea is placed in your unconscious mind your unconscious processes will try to find a way of making it happen, of turning it into reality.

Our inner beliefs create our outer reality and if that is something which gives us discomfort or suffering then it will continue to do so, sometimes increasing in the intensity, until we get the message and understand that we need to change, we need to see things differently.

EXPERIENCES CREATE BELIEFS
AND THEN
BELIEFS CREATE EXPERIENCES

CENTRAL BELIEFS

These beliefs can usually be found in general statements which reflect our outlook on the world. We are not always consciously aware of them, but they determine and dominate our perceptions, thoughts and responses to events and situations. It can be very useful to be aware of some of these beliefs because they can have a very strong and direct influence on our relationship with food. They have the potential power to create or sabotage our attempts to lose weight. They give very straightforward orders to the brain. One change in your central beliefs can have a very powerful effect on all areas of your life.

For instance, if one of your central beliefs about life is that you can never change, then that is the message your unconscious will give to your body. You may spend years and fortunes on diets and weight loss schemes trying to make your body change when it is under strict directions to stay exactly the same.

WHAT YOU SEE IS A REFLECTION
OF WHAT YOU BELIEVE

If you were to imagine two people, let's call them Light and Heavy, who each see the world very differently, then they would be looking at the world through very different internal windows.

OUR BELIEF SYSTEM
Our window on the world

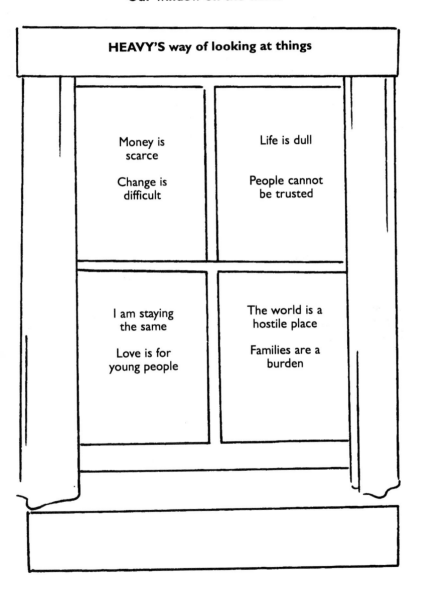

HEAVY'S way of looking at things

Money is
scarce

Change is
difficult

Life is dull

People cannot
be trusted

I am staying
the same

Love is for
young people

The world is a
hostile place

Families are a
burden

OUR BELIEF SYSTEM
Our window on the world

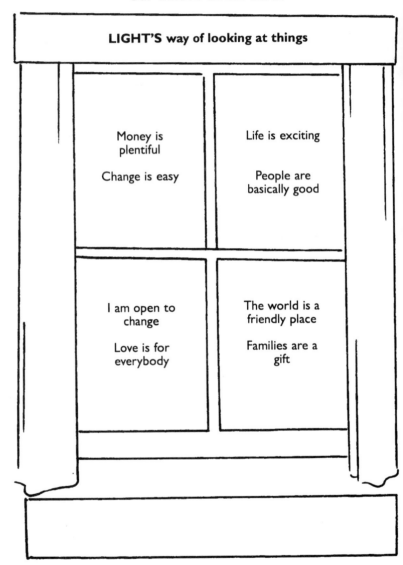

LIGHT'S way of looking at things

Money is
plentiful

Change is easy

Life is exciting

People are
basically good

I am open to
change

Love is for
everybody

The world is a
friendly place

Families are a
gift

IS YOUR BELIEF SYSTEM WORKING FOR OR AGAINST YOU IN YOUR SEARCH FOR PERMANENT WEIGHT LOSS?

SELF-LIMITING BELIEFS

Both our central beliefs and our specific beliefs can be very self-limiting. It is essential to identify and change such self-limiting beliefs if we are to achieve permanent weight loss.

You may recognise some of the following self-limiting beliefs and how they prevent you from successfully and permanently losing weight.

Examples of self-limiting beliefs that can be a barrier to permanent weight loss

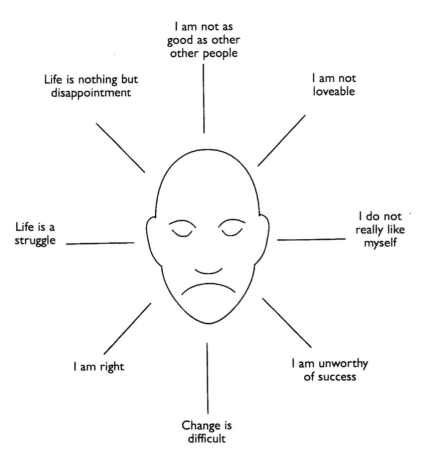

I'm not as good as other people......
- if I lose weight it would make me look as good as other people and that would make me their equal, but I am inferior so I must not lose weight.

I'm stupid......
- I am not clever enough to follow a diet or a healthy eating plan. I will continue to eat the wrong foods even though I know they are wrong.

I'm not loveable......
- if my body looked different I might look attractive and that would make me look loveable, so I must stay looking unattractive and overweight.

I'm too old......
- how can I change now, it is too late to bother looking at myself, I will stay overweight.

I really don't like myself......
- I will not do something caring, like looking after my body, for somebody I do not like.

I'm unworthy of success......
- I do not deserve to be any lighter, I do not deserve or expect my attempts at losing weight to be successful.

Change is difficult......
- so losing weight must always be difficult. No matter how hard I work at it I will never lose weight easily.

Success has a price......
- everything in my life is going well, career, relationship, being a parent, there must be a price to pay for all this and that price is my inability to lose weight.

I am right......
- I will always be the weight I am, and no information, healthy eating plan, opportunity or different way of seeing things will ever help me change my weight.

Nobody really cares......
- so why should I bother about my body?

Others are more important than me......
- so I put all my energy into caring and pleasing others, rather than paying attention to my own needs and using my caring to look after my body and lose weight.

Life is a struggle......
- so attempts at losing weight will always be a struggle, if I were ever successful the struggle would be over, so I must never be successful.

Life is nothing but disappointment......
- so my expectation of disappointment is constantly fulfilled by my failure to lose weight.

Fat is my fate......
- I know I am overweight, but I am just meant to be and there is nothing I can do to change it.

EXCUSES

Nobody knows your excuses for not losing weight permanently as well as you do.

e.g.
    I will lose weight when.....
    I will not lose weight until.....
    I could lose weight but.....
    I cannot keep weight off because.....

Write them down now. It is important that you do this.

All the negative thoughts.
All the reasons you give to other people.
All the reasons you give to yourself.

All these excuses are self-limiting beliefs.

Imagine how successful you would be in losing weight permanently if you never allowed yourself to use any of these excuses again!

SELF-LIMITING BELIEFS ARE THE MOST COMMON AND FUNDAMENTAL BARRIER TO SUCCESSFUL AND PERMANENT WEIGHT LOSS

FINDING YOUR BELIEFS

There are some general guidelines to help you as you move on from here. It is important that you use them, they will make your progress even more effective.

1. Take the time that you need to do the exercises thoroughly. If you spend less than one week on this section on beliefs then you are rushing and this will bring limited results. You have spent your whole lifetime gathering these beliefs and storing many of them at an unconscious level, so give yourself the necessary time to be in touch with them.

2. Write things down, including any feelings that may come up. This enables you to focus more closely on the area you are dealing with. It also allows you to follow a train of thought, creatively and constructively and follow any clues that you come across as to how you might find a new way of looking at things.

3. Once you have started the process of looking at your belief system, your unconscious mind will continue it, even when your conscious processing has finished. You know how sometimes you rack your brain to think of somebody's name and then suddenly, hours later, the name you have been looking for pops into your mind. Well, that is often how the unconscious mind works, so keep a notebook near at hand.

TRAPDOOR

If you are a yo-yo dieter, or feel that you have lacked motivation and commitment to losing weight in the past, then there is a danger that you will skip over these simple steps to permanent weight loss and wonder why nothing changes.

If you feel some resistance to starting, ask yourself – why?

Are you just using one of your old excuses?
Or perhaps one of your self-limiting beliefs is stopping you. If it is, then thank it for showing itself. Make a note of it so that you can set about changing it.
You may hear yourself saying:

- This looks like hard work
- I'll do it later
- Oh, I know all this, I don't need to do it
- I don't want to think about this just now
- I don't think this is going to work
- I cannot be bothered

If any of these or similiar thoughts go through your mind, then just think when you have said these things before and what they have stopped you achieving or enjoying in the past.

You may well have said the same about losing weight!

If you believe that this will be hard work, then it will be. If you see it as child's play, then it will be and we all know how much children enjoy playing!

If you wish to stop here for now, then do, but fix a time when you are going to carry on AND THEN STICK TO IT!

THE BEST OF INTENTIONS REMAIN THE BEST OF INTENTIONS UNLESS THEY ARE FOLLOWED BY ACTION.

GETTING TO KNOW YOUR BELIEFS

MIXED BELIEFS

It is not at all unusual to have a positive and self-limiting belief about the same topic. Most of us have them about several topics. We then have what we call mixed beliefs. The unconscious is faced with two directions in which to move. It cannot move in two different directions at the same time and so it stands still.

Mixed beliefs about weight loss bring mixed results and usually the result is no weight loss at all.

e.g.

I want to be slim, but being attractive will threaten my relationship.
It is best to lose weight slowly, but I want to lose weight quickly.
Dieting does not work, but dieting will make me lose weight.
I want to have what I believe food will give me, but I want to have what I believe successful dieting will give me.

Whilst you attempt to hold these two beliefs at the same time you will find only conflict, frustration, self-criticism, pain, and a sense of failure.

By letting go of your self-limiting belief you eliminate your mixed belief and you are able to go forward.

As has been mentioned, your central beliefs can often be those which are stopping you losing weight. As you enjoy exploring the following topics you can find yourself identifying your beliefs about each of them.

If you have temporary difficulty identifying your beliefs then completing the following statements will help you.

For example:

CHANGE is.....*difficult*
    has brought me......*regrets*
    will bring me......*more regrets*
    makes me feel......*scared*
    allows me to......*become myself*
    stops me......*standing still*
    enables me to......*achieve*
    always......*gets me excited*

Positive belief:
Change is exciting, with change I can achieve things and become myself.

How can this positive belief help me lose weight?
Permanent weight loss is a change, I can achieve it, I can find it exciting, it will allow me to become myself.

Self limiting belief:
Change is difficult and will bring regrets.

How could this self-limiting belief be stopping me losing weight?
Losing weight permanently is a change, so I will find it difficult, it will bring me regrets so I prefer to avoid it.

Not all the following topics will necessarily contain both positive and self-limiting beliefs. If you cannot find any about a particular subject, that is just fine — move on to the next — but come back later and go through any you have left out, something may come to you when you look at them again.

TRAPDOOR

Take your time. Even though you may be eager to move on, do not be tempted to rush. The more time you spend with yourself, the more effective the process will be.

So now go ahead and work through the following topics for yourself:

CHANGE is.....
        has brought me.....
        can bring me.....
        makes me feel.....
        allows me to.....
        stops me.....
        enables me to.....
        always.....

Positive belief.....

How can this positive belief help me lose weight....?

Self-limiting belief.....

How could this self-limiting belief be stopping me losing weight....?

EXERCISE is.....
               has brought me.....
               can bring me.....
               makes me feel.....
               allows me to.....
               stops me.....
               enables me to.....
               always.....

Positive belief.....

How can this positive belief help me lose weight....?

Self-limiting belief.....

How could this self-limiting belief be stopping me losing weight....?

SUCCESS is.....
               has brought me.....
               can bring me.....
               makes me feel.....
               allows me to.....
               stops me.....
               enables me to.....
               always.....

Positive belief.....

How can this positive belief help me lose weight.....?

Self-limiting belief.....

How could this self-limiting belief be stopping me losing weight .....?

PLEASURE is.....
   has brought me.....
   can bring me.....
   makes me feel.....
   allows me to.....
   stops me.....
   enables me to.....
   always.....

Positive belief.....

How can this positive belief help me lose weight.....?

Self-limiting belief.....

How could this self-limiting belief be stopping me losing weight.....?

WORK is.....
   has brought me.....
   can bring me.....
   makes me feel.....
   allows me to.....
   stops me.....
   enables me to.....
   always.....

Positive belief.....

How can this positive belief help me lose weight.....?

Self-limiting belief.....

How could this self-limiting belief be stopping me losing weight.....?

HONESTY is.....
   has brought me.....
   can bring me.....
   makes me feel.....
   allows me to.....
   stops me.....
   enables me to.....
   always.....

Positive belief.....

How can this positive belief help me lose weight.....?

Self-limiting belief.....

How could this self-limiting belief be stopping me losing weight.....?

TRAPDOOR

Do not rush. Give each topic the time it needs. Do not try to do too much at one session.

ENTHUSIASM is.....
> has brought me.....
> can bring me.....
> makes me feel.....
> allows me to.....
> stops me.....
> enables me to.....
> always.....

Positive belief.....

How can this positive belief help me lose weight.....?

Self-limiting belief.....

How could this self-limiting belief be stopping me losing weight.....?

FAILURE is.....
> has brought me.....
> can bring me.....
> makes me feel.....
> allows me to.....
> stops me.....
> enables me to.....
> always.....

Positive belief.....

How can this positive belief help me lose weight.....?

Self-limiting belief.....

How could this self-limiting belief be stopping me losing weight.....?

SELF-DISCIPLINE is.....
        has brought me.....
        can bring me.....
        makes me feel......
        allows me to.....
        stops me.....
        enables me to.....
        always.....

Positive belief.....

How can this positive belief help me lose weight.....?

Self-limiting belief.....

How could this self-limiting belief be stopping me losing weight.....?

PERSISTENCE is.....
        has brought me.....
        can bring me.....
        makes me feel.....
        allows me to.....
        stops me.....
        enables me to.....
        always.....

Positive belief.....

How can this positive belief help me lose weight.....?

Self-limiting belief.....

How could this self-limiting belief be stopping me losing weight.....?

HEALTH is.....
> has brought me.....
> can bring me.....
> makes me feel.....
> allows me to.....
> stops me.....
> enables me to.....
> always.....

Positive belief.....

How can this positive belief help me lose weight.....?

Self-limiting belief.....

How could this self-limiting belief be stopping me losing weight .....?

LOVE is.....
> has brought me.....
> can bring me.....
> makes me feel.....
> allows me to.....
> stops me.....
> enables me to.....
> always.....

Positive belief.....

How could this positive belief help me lose weight.....?

Self-limiting belief.....

How could this self-limiting belief be stopping me losing weight.....?

A RELATIONSHIP is.....
> has brought me.....
> can bring me.....
> makes me feel.....
> allows me to.....
> stops me.....
> enables me to.....
> always.....

Positive belief.....

How could this positive belief help me lose weight.....?

Self-limiting belief.....

How could this self-limiting belief be stopping me losing weight.....?

RESPONSIBILITY is.....
        has brought me.....
        can bring me.....
        makes me feel......
        allows me to.....
        stops me.....
        enables me to.....
        always.....

Positive belief.....

How could this positive belief help me lose weight.....?

Self-limiting belief.....

How could this self-limiting belief be stopping me losing weight .....?

COMMITMENT is.....
        has brought me.....
        can bring me.....
        makes me feel.....
        allows me to.....
        stops me.....
        enables me to.....
        always.....

Positive belief.....

How could this positive belief help me lose weight.....?

Self-limiting belief.....

How could this self-limiting belief be stopping me losing weight.....?

My self-limiting beliefs that can stop me losing weight

Write down your self-limiting beliefs in the bubbles

My positive beliefs that can help me lose weight

Write down your positive beliefs in the bubbles

BEWARE OF OTHERS' OPINIONS. THEY CAN EASILY BECOME YOUR BELIEFS

BELIEFS ABOUT WEIGHT LOSS

Identifying our beliefs about food and weight loss, in addition to our beliefs about ourselves and life in general, is essential if we are to move on to a new set of beliefs which will empower us to achieve permanent weight loss.

TRAPDOOR

There is no rush. Do not be impatient. You are building new foundations in your relationship with food.
You have taken years to establish your present one so enjoy and be thorough in planning a new one.

Again it is necessary to look closely at some particular topics.

Take one topic at a time and complete the following statements and then see if you have a positive belief, or a self-limiting belief and how that self-limiting belief could be stopping you losing weight.

MY BODY is.....
        has brought me.....
        can bring me.....
        makes me feel.....
        allows me to.....
        stops me.....
        enables me to.....
        always.....

Positive belief.....

How can this positive belief help me lose weight.....?

Self-limiting belief.....

How could this self-limiting belief be stopping me losing weight.....?

BEING SLIM is......
     has brought me.....
     can bring me.....
     makes me feel.....
     allows me to.....
     stops me.....
     enables me to.....
     always.....

Positive belief.....

How can this positive belief help me lose weight.....?

Self-limiting belief.....

How could this self-limiting belief be stopping me losing weight.....?

BEING FAT is.....
     has brought me.....
     can bring me.....
     makes me feel.....
     allows me to.....
     stops me.....
     enables me to.....
     always.....

Positive belief.....

How can this positive belief help me lose weight.....?

Self-limiting belief.....

How could this self-limiting belief be stopping me losing weight.....?

LOSING WEIGHT is.....
     has brought me.....
     can bring me.....
     makes me feel.....
     allows me to.....
     stops me.....
     enables me to.....
     always.....

Positive belief.....

How can this positive belief help me lose weight.....?

Self-limiting belief.....

How could this self-limiting belief be stopping me losing weight .....?

GAINING WEIGHT is.....
               has brought me.....
               can bring me.....
               makes me feel.....
               allows me to.....
               stops me.....
               enables me to.....
               always.....

Positive belief.....

How can this positive belief help me lose weight.....?

Self-limiting belief.....

How could this self-limiting belief be stopping me losing weight.....?

DIETING is.....
               has brought me.....
               can bring me.....
               makes me feel.....
               allows me to.....
               stops me.....
               enables me to.....
               always.....

Positive belief.....

How can this positive belief help me lose weight.....?

Self-limiting belief.....

How could this self-limiting belief be stopping me losing weight .....?

FOOD is.....
  has brought me.....
  can bring me.....
  makes me feel.....
  allows me to.....
  stops me.....
  enables me to.....
  always.....

Positive belief.....

How can this positive belief help me lose weight.....?

Self-limiting belief.....

How could this self-limiting belief be stopping me losing weight.....?

EATING is....
  has brought me.....
  can bring me.....
  makes me feel.....
  allows me to.....
  stops me.....
  enables me to....
  always.....

Positive belief.....

How can this positive belief help me lose weight.....?

Self-limiting belief.....

How could this be stopping me losing weight.....?

EATING THE WRONG FOODS is.....
  has brought me.....
  can bring me.....
  makes me feel.....
  allows me to.....
  stops me.....
  enables me to.....
  always.....

Positive belief.........

How can this positive belief help me lose weight.........?

Self-limiting belief........

How could this be stopping me losing weight.......?

EATING HEALTHILY is.............
                        has brought me........
                        can bring me........
                        makes me feel.......
                        allows me to.........
                        stops me.....
                        enables me to.......
                        always.........

Positive belief.......

How can this positive belief help me lose weight.........?

Self-limiting belief........

How could this be stopping me losing weight ....?

Write down your self limiting beliefs about weight loss

Write down your positive beliefs about weight loss

LETTING GO OF SELF-LIMITING BELIEFS

Take one of your self-limiting beliefs which has stopped you losing weight and which you would like to change.

Write the belief down and then work through the following questions.

Here we can use as an example the self-limiting belief:

LIFE IS A STRUGGLE

1. Where/who did I get this belief from?
My parents

2. Why did I choose to make it mine?
(Do not criticise, judge or blame yourself for having chosen or maintained a belief. It served a positive purpose and was an attempt to meet your needs at the time.)
It made it okay to moan about things.

3. What benefits did the belief bring me at the time or in the short term?
I agreed with my parents, I saw things their way. They would always be on my side when things went wrong.

4. How has this belief affected my life in the past, in terms of family, friends, emotions, relationships, career, self-esteem, confidence, motivation and weight?
I have always needed the support of my parents
I have mixed with other people who struggle
I struggle to get on at work
I struggle to speak my mind
I struggle to express my emotions
I struggle to lose weight

5. How is it affecting me at present?
Everything seems so difficult I have almost given up trying.

6. If I hang on to this belief what might it cost me in the future?
I will achieve very little of what I want in life.

7. Do I really want to keep this belief?
NO!

All these questions raise doubts about the fundamental value and use of a belief.

They also give us a clue as to how we can find a more useful belief, for no belief can be taken away without it being replaced.

WHAT WILL REPLACE THE OLD BELIEF?

The new belief has to be positive, the unconscious mind has to focus on creating something new. It is no use saying: *I am not going to struggle any more*, because the unconscious mind will immediately re-run your past struggles and that is where your focus will be. A much more useful belief in this situation would be: *Life is a game*.

The most powerful new beliefs are those that are positive and stated in the present.

If the belief is in the future e.g. "I will begin to treat life as a game," then that is where the reality will stay, always in the future and never in the present.

So keep your new beliefs in the present:

eg. Change is possible
   Exercise is fun
   I am choosing to be successful
   I am choosing to take care of myself
   I am open to new ideas
   It is okay to make mistakes, they are just opportunities to learn
   I can have a balanced diet and really enjoy it.
   I can have health and pleasure at the same time.
   My body deserves healthy food.
   I am in charge of my life
   I can achieve whatever I choose to achieve

As you find a new belief that you sense will work for you rather than against you, write it down on the page of new beliefs.

Here are some examples of beliefs that people have changed.

Something always happens to stop me.
to
I can overcome challenges and learn from them.

Any improvement is only temporary.
to
I can enjoy this step forward and welcome the prospect of the next one.

I could lose weight, but........
to
I can lose weight and........

Other people are more capable than me
to
I can achieve whatever I choose to achieve

Success has a price
to
Success is a choice

Changing self-limiting beliefs is the most important step along your pathway to permanent weight loss. Once you believe you can be successful, everything else starts to move towards that success.

WHEN I BEGIN TO SEE ME DIFFERENTLY
I WILL BEGIN TO SEE FOOD DIFFERENTLY

MAKING THE NEW BELIEF YOURS

A new belief will only become yours fully if it is stronger than the old belief.

TRAPDOOR

In the early stages, if we do not re-enforce and tune in to the new belief everyday the likelihood is that we will revert to the old unwanted belief.
Merely finding the new belief is not enough, you really have to own it, really make it yours.

There are a number of ways of doing this. Use them all, but practise most frequently those which you feel work best for you.

i) Reaffirm strongly your commitment to change and to self responsibilty. Remember this is your choice, only you can decide to do it and nobody else can do it for you.

ii) **Pretend: Act as if your new belief is already true.** As you strengthen your new belief, so your thoughts, emotions, behaviour and body will follow, until your new behaviour becomes automatic.

iii) **Imagine how you would behave if your new belief were already true and then do things that way.** Picture an image of yourself, or see yourself on a television or film screen. Watch yourself acting in the future when your new belief is really part of you. How you will react differently, and do things in new ways. Make the picure of yourself stronger, bigger, clearer, brighter, more colourful.   Enjoy the expression that you see on your face.
Step inside that new you, with that new belief and let the good feeling that it gives you spread throughout your whole body. Repeat this every day.
Remember. SEEING IS BELIEVING and the unconscious mind believes what is real and what is vividly imagined.

iv) **Write down what the new belief is bringing you, in terms of health, confidence, motivation, control, and self-esteem.** Be aware of the sensation of freedom, wellbeing and pleasure it gives you.

v) **Affirm your new belief, using words that give you a positive sense of the reality that you are going to create.** If you can imagine your change as you say the affirmation, then it is the right affirmation for you. Make sure the affirmations are positive, in the present and on-going.

e.g. **I am learning to grow in a new and different way.**
     I am enjoying the process of change.
     I am becoming the person I choose to be.
     As I am learning to let go, so is my body.

There is an extremely powerful way of strengthening your affirmations at an unconscious level. This was devised by top Irish psychotherapist Daniel Longridge and is called *subliminal visual stimuli*.
The process is simple.

a) Find your affirmation.
b) Close your eyes and really be with that affirmation until you find a visual image of it coming to your mind.
c) Draw a very simple version of that picture on brightly coloured card or paper about postcard size.
d) Take the first letter of each word of your affirmation and write it clearly below the picture. e.g. *I am enjoying changing my eating habit.*
=IAECMEH

e) Make about six copies and place them where you will see them during the day: fridge door, bathroom, on top of the television, next to the kettle etc.

f) It does not matter whether you are consciously aware of seeing these or not, they will be very strongly reinforcing the message of your affirmation.

vi) **Practise your new belief every day as many times and in as many ways as you can.** Write it, think it, feel it, walk it, see it, taste it, imagine it, behave it, talk it, own it, smile it, dream it, wallow in it, strengthen it, build it higher, wider, make the colours of your image more vivid. LIVE IT in every way that you can.

vii) **Remember if there is no change in feeling, there is no change. Notice how you feel.** Strengthen that feeling by staying with it, allow it to flow and move through every part of your body as it gets stronger and stronger.

You get good at what you practise. Find out which of the above strategies works most effectively for you and get into the habit of using it everyday. Eventually you will notice how your new belief operates without you being aware of it at all.

A KEY TO PERMANENT WEIGHT LOSS IS TO EAT WITH NO REFERENCE TO THE PAST.

Human beings are unique in that they often keep going up the wrong route, even though they have discovered a better one. Because the old route seems wider and more familiar we let ourselves drift up it even though in the long term we know it is wrong. We have to stay aware of what we are doing until the new belief becomes automatic.

IF YOU REPEAT IT YOU KEEP IT

Remember, changing a belief is about finding what is not working for you, noticing how it is affecting your life, finding an alternative and practising it until it becomes a habit.

5.

STEP TWO:
YOUR THOUGHTS

**WHETHER YOU THINK YOU CAN
OR WHETHER YOU THINK YOU CAN'T
YOU ARE PROBABLY RIGHT**
(Henry Ford)

Take a moment to think of a pleasant time you had recently - it may have been a holiday, a night out or whatever. Recall enjoying yourself and how that felt.
Do not rush.

You chose exactly what thoughts you just had. You brought them into your mind.

We have control over our thoughts, they are not just something which appear from nowhere.

When you had those thoughts you were also in touch with a particular feeling, a feeling of pleasure.

So not only do we choose our thoughts, we also have control over our thoughts.
Our thoughts create our feelings.
This puts us in a very powerful position.

So often we neglect this power completely, allowing our fearful and negative thought processes to determine our feelings and our behaviour.
We allow self-criticism and self-sabotage to undermine so much of what we are capable of achieving.
This includes weight loss.
If we overcome and change our self-limiting beliefs, and our thoughts are consistent with our positive beliefs, then the way forward to successful and permanent weight loss is clear.
To allow our thoughts to come into line with our positive beliefs, we have to change some of our familiar and automatic negative thought processes.

What are your thoughts creating at present?

Our thoughts cover many subjects during the course of a day. It is useful to see where our thoughts are taking us at present, so we can see where we need to change them.

BECOMING AWARE

TRAPDOOR

Treat this as an exercise. It is very important that you do these exercises, not merely read them and consider them done. Just as you may not be too keen on exercising your body, you may not be used to exercising your mind!

This is an exercise in awareness, you have to experience it if you are going to truly learn new ways of thinking and listening to your thoughts.

As Confucius said:

I hear and I forget;
I see and I remember;
I do and I understand.

Spread this exercise over two days.

1) Do not make any attempt to change your thought processes yet.
Spend one whole day being aware of how many times your thoughts focus on the problems associated with losing weight. Just write a *I* each time this happens, either here in the book or on a piece of paper. For instance:
Each time you run into inner conflict about whether or not you should have food.
Each time you think of not liking your body.
Each time you criticise yourself or judge yourself.
Each time you compare yourself to others.
Each time you tell yourself off for having eaten something you should not have.
Each time you mention something negative about your weight to others.
Etc.

2) Again, without making any effort to change anything yet, spend the next day noting how many times you focus on enjoying the solutions to losing weight and feeling good about yourself for having achieved them.

Now compare the two.

Most of us spend 90 per cent of our time focusing on the problems and difficulties of a situation and only 10 per cent looking at the solution.

Remember:

YOU GET GOOD AT WHAT YOU PRACTISE

WHAT YOU FOCUS ON CREATES YOUR REALITY

If you are choosing to focus your thoughts on the problems and difficulties of losing weight then that is where you will stay. You will get very good at creating, reinforcing and hanging on to these difficulties.

IF YOU WORRY ABOUT SOMETHING LONG ENOUGH, THE WORRY WILL JUST GET STRONGER.

Those beliefs and thoughts which have brought you to where you are now, will not take you forward to where you want to go. There has to be a change.
A new way of thinking is needed.
This cannot be done by dwelling on old thoughts and expectations of failure – we have to do something new.

IF YOUR THOUGHTS ARE ABOUT WHAT YOU CANNOT CONTROL, THEN YOU WILL CONTINUE NOT CONTROLLING IT.

GETTING THE WEIGHT OFF YOUR MIND WITH THE ONE WEEK HEALTHY THINKING PLAN

Follow this plan for one week.
It will take commitment, but each time you stop your negative thoughts and actions about weight loss, you will be opening up and reinforcing a new way of thinking.

1) For one week do not allow yourself to focus on the problems associated with weight loss, only on the solutions.

2) To find solutions and a more useful way of looking at things, ask yourself the following questions when you find yourself choosing to have a negative thought.

How could I look at this differently?
How is this situation an opportunity to learn?
What belief do I need to change, in order to let go of this thought?
What can I do differently to stop this thought coming to me again?

These questions will provide you with an opportunity to cut short the possibility of prolonging negative thoughts.

3) Take time to think of new ways of seeing things and doing things. Do not see yourself with a problem, but only with a temporary difficulty. If you choose to spend enough time with it, you will certainly find an answer.

4) If you find yourself lapsing and spending time with a negative thought do not give yourself a hard time. Remember, lapsing is an essential part of learning – so long as you re-focus yourself and move forward.

5) If you find yourself stuck with a negative thought that will not go away, then set aside some time to really investigate it, to discover where it has come from, what purpose it is serving. When you see clearly that you no longer need it, let it go. It serves you no purpose other than to keep you where you are.

There is no doubt that you will need commitment and persistence with this healthy-thinking plan, but the benefits will be enormous if you persist.
As well as giving you a new way of looking at things, it will also strengthen, support and encourage the change in your relationship with food.

**PERSIST
AND YOU WILL
TURN LAZINESS INTO ACTION
FEAR INTO ACHIEVEMENT
SUCCESS INTO HABIT.**

Of course it is a challenge. Change and risk are a challenge. They can both bring you permanent weight loss.
The value of any process is in how often you use it.

IF YOU REPEAT IT YOU KEEP IT

Knowing what to do is fine – but you have to do it!

YOUR INNER CRITIC – the things we say to ourselves.

Your inner critic found its beginning in your childhood. We are still carrying messages around in our heads, both verbal and non-verbal, which we received from significant adults in our lives, such as teachers and parents. These messages are replaying memories of times when we believed or had been told that we had done something wrong or bad. These messages are often taken in and seen as the truth, totally believed and played over and over in the mind of the child. The messages you received may have served some purpose in moulding your behaviour and attitude at the time, but the negative critic we carry with us into adulthood saps our energy and drains our confidence. It destroys our self-esteem and ability to succeed and achieve.

Your inner-critic is the greatest saboteur of your attempts to lose weight.

When your negative self-critic is at work undermining your confidence, motivation and self-esteem it may be saying many different things to you.

You are stupid
You will never succeed
You are boring to listen to
You will never lose weight
You are unattractive
You must be perfect
etc, etc.

There is a continual inner dialogue going on all day long and somewhere in it your negative self-critic is at work.
Hiding away and secreting itself amongst your many other thoughts, your critic eats away at your peace of mind and your sense of worth.

EXPOSING YOUR INNER CRITIC

One of the simplest ways of weakening your critic's power is to take away its veil of secrecy and bring it into the open.

In a similiar way to identifying your thoughts, now spend some time listening very closely to your inner critic. What sort of things do you say to yourself if you get something wrong, if you forget something, if you eat or say something you think you shouldn't?

Make a note of these as you go along and fill them in on the diagram. Write down the actual language you use, how rude and abusive you are to yourself.

My inner critic. The insulting, negative things I say to myself Write them in below

STOP SAYING THEM!

Once you have got used to listening to this inner voice, be aware of it each time that you hear it. Do not let it work in secret again. At first you will need to pay very close attention and concentrate but after a little while you will clearly recognise when it is your critic talking. Sometimes the critic does not use words to get the harmful message to you, but instead uses images, pictures and memories of past failures. Be aware of these also.

To give yourself the freedom to move forward to permanent weight loss it is necessary to silence this critic, to silence its voice and to take away its power. Being aware of it is the first step, then you can begin to take away its power.

ANSWERING BACK

There are various ways of silencing the critic.

Try these and discover which is the most effective for you:

1) WHAT IS IT COSTING YOU TO LISTEN?

Listen briefly to the message your critic is giving you and recall times that you have listened to this in the past and what it has cost you. Think what it might be costing you in the present and what it might cost you in the future.

For example your critic may say:

If you are going to lose weight by eating heathily then you have to do it perfectly, one little slip and it will be just another of your failures.

So what has it cost, this need to be perfect all the time?

Disappointment at excellent exam results?
Giving up a sport because you did not always win?
Leaving a relationship because you lost an argument?
Unfairly attacking people at the slightest hint of criticism?
Feeling a failure even though you know you are a good parent?

When you are aware of this cost to yourself, you very firmly tell your critic:

You are not worth listening to because.......
and choose a phrase which sums up all that it has cost you.

2) THE FULL FRONTAL

It can be very rude to you, so do the same back.
When you hear it talking to you, give it straight back. Really mean it!
Say, with the strongest and most meaningful voice that you can find:

SHUT UP!
GET LOST!
YOU ARE SO BORING!
YOU ARE PATHETIC!
GO AND FIND SOMEBODY ELSE TO LISTEN TO YOU!
YOU ARE A LIAR AND YOU KNOW IT!
BE QUIET YOU SILLY LITTLE THING!
GET OUT OF MY LIFE!
etc.

If you choose to use stronger language then do so. Most people do!

3) THE VOICE OF COMPASSION

Reply to your critic using understanding and compassion.

Critic: *You are stupid*
Reply: *You are wrong. I may have made a few mistakes along the way, but so does everybody. I have a right to do that. It is the best way of learning.*

Critic: *You are lazy*
Reply: *You are wrong again. I need to rest, just as everybody does. It will give me more energy for the future.*

All these exercises are about learning to disagree with and reject your early childhood negative messages.

They can be used as many times as necessary. They will be effective in silencing the critic for varying lengths of time. Sometimes varying the message is more powerful than repeating it. Each time you are aware of your critic and you shut it up you are eroding its power to undermine you.

**Answering your critic
What would you say back to it?
Fill in the arrows**

SAYING GOOD THINGS TO YOURSELF

We have a choice about what we say to ourselves in our heads. Instead of attacking ourselves constantly we can be supporting and nurturing. We can take care of ourselves with compassionate thoughts. Finding these words need not be difficult.

1) What good things do you say to yourself? Think of them and write them down.

The nurturing inner voice. Supporting, caring and encouraging things I can say to myself

2) Imagine that you had a very understanding, kind person or parent with you. What sort of things would they be saying to you? They would not only forgive you for any mistake, but recognise that you have needs to meet the same as everybody else.
Write down what they might say to you.

3) To develop this new understanding, supportive inner-talk needs a new way of thinking. It is time to let go of judgement and criticism.

4) Fill in the picture with supportive self-talk. Above all be compassionate and supportive.

eg.
I am not going be hard on myself, I do not deserve it.
I am a good and caring person.
I do my best when I know how.
I care.
I am special and unique.
I am capable of success and I choose it.
I am good at what I do.

USE THEM AT EVERY OPPORTUNITY.

SHAKING LOOSE FROM *SHOULD*

Should is one of the most used words in the negative critic's weaponry.
Letting go of the unwanted *shoulds* again greatly reduces its power.
The more you reduce its power, the easier it will be for you to move forward.
Your critic picks up *shoulds* not only from your childhood but also from colleagues, bosses, advertising and even friends!

FINDING YOUR UNWANTED *SHOULDS*

Consider what *shoulds* you might have around the following subjects:

Partner   Clothes
Children   Food
Friends   Eating
Self-discipline   Health
Appearance   Self-improvement
Exercise   Organisation
Alcohol   Weight

Negative shoulds that keep me stuck

Write them in

Some of these *shoulds* may be very useful:

e.g. *I should take care of my health*
      I should spend quality time with my family

But there will be others which are negative, and these are the ones that your critic uses against you:

e.g. *I should never make mistakes*
      I should always do what others want

QUESTIONING YOUR *SHOULDS*

Once you have identified your negative *shoulds* – those that your critic attacks and criticises and makes you feel guilty with – you can begin to question them and change them.

1) What words are you using?

If you are using words of complete certainty, such as *never, always, have to* etc, then replace them with words which allow for an element of flexibilty, such as, *prefer, would, rather*. This introduces an element of choice.

e.g. *I prefer not to make mistakes.*
      I would rather do what others want.

This will help you question if the choice is truly yours. You may decide that it is okay to make mistakes as long as they are seen as opportunities to learn.Sometimes you prefer to please yourself, rather than do what others want.

Use this process next time you hear your critic using a *should.*

2) Does the *should* make sense?

What will the long-term consequences be? Will it cause anybody, including yourself, any pain or harm?
If the answer is *yes* then this is definitely a *should* to let go of.
e.g. *I should never apologise.*
In the long-term this may create resentment and frustration from yourself and others. It may stop you getting close in a relationship.

3) Does the *should* feel comfortable?

Does it take your feelings into consideration?
Do you want to be this person you *should* be?
If not, it is a *should* to let go of.

e.g. *I should always please others.*

In the long-term this may see you never giving enough time to yourself
and thereby not caring for your health.

SHUTTING OFF THE *SHOULDS*

There can be real satisfaction in shutting up the *should*. It is disarming
your critic of one of its most powerful tools.

**AS YOU CHANGE THE WAY YOU THINK, SO YOU NOTICE
A CHANGE IN THE WAY YOU FEEL.**

1) It is important to have prepared a reply for when you hear your inner
critic giving you a negative *should* message that you no longer wish to
hear.

2) Say it as many times as necessary until the critic shuts up and
eventually stops using the *should*.

3) The strongest answer will have two parts to it.
The first part is about why you took up the *should* in the first place.
e.g.   To be accepted by a friend or family member.
       To be approved of by somebody.
       To feel safe and secure.
       So that people would not get angry with you.

The second part of the reply lets the critic know why this *should* does
not fit your life now, the demands of the *should* are not something you
wish to do any longer.

So:
You should not make mistakes.
Can be answered with:
***My father always got angry when I made a mistake. He wanted me
to be perfect but now I know that mistakes are a vital part of learning.***

You should be thin.
Can be answered with:
My mother always wanted me to be what she could not be. Whilst I am dieting she is happy. I can now choose to be the weight I want to be, but it is my choice if I choose to stay slim.

You could do better in life.
Can be answered with:
My father always valued people by their job, not by the person themselves. I am happy in what I am doing and that is more valuable to me than what other people think.

4) Choose the strongest negative *should* that your critic attacks you with and work out your reply. Use it consistently every time you hear the *should*. If you do not answer back you are agreeing with the critic.

Once you have silenced one *should* move on to others.

AFFIRMATIONS

Another way to change the process of thought is to re-enforce the positive intentions you have and the powerful inner resources you have working for you.

A simple but highly effective way of doing this is with affirmations. You will already be acquainted with these through your work on your belief system.

Affirmations are simple positive statements.
They are repeated many, many times. The unconscious mind will always follow the strongest of two ideas, and if the positive idea is strengthened, it eventually becomes the one which is followed automatically.
Our body is then free to follow these positively focused thoughts and to be in harmony with them.
Affirmations alone are unlikely to achieve weight loss, but are highly effective when beliefs, thoughts, feelings and behaviour are all being aligned to work together.
Affirmations can make you feel calm, focused and positive in your belief in achieving permanent weight loss.
Affirmations have a very strong influence on our thoughts and our feelings, these two cannot be separated, for emotions come from our thoughts.

CREATING AND USING YOUR OWN AFFIRMATIONS

1) Make a list of all the negative thoughts that you have about your desire and ability to lose weight.
This might read:

I am not motivated enough
I do not have staying power
I am stuffing down my feelings
I am out of control
I cannot resist chocolate
I am too weak-willed
etc, etc,

2) Now turn these around and write down the positive version of each of these.

Make sure that they are always stated in the present:

I am motivated
I have staying power
I can express my feelings
I am in control
I can resist chocolate
I am strong-willed.

Write your affirmations down here:

3) Select one of these positive statements and choose a quiet time to look closely at it.

You can sit down and write it out or put on some music and stay with the thought. Any negative feelings or thoughts you have about it, just let them come. Acknowledge your resistance to accepting this statement.

As you allow the resistance to come out (you can write your negative thoughts down or just let the feelings rise) keep repeating firmly but gently to yourself the positive statement. Let the negative thoughts and feelings flow away from you as you repeat it.

You are beginning to own it.

4) Repeat it at every available opportunity at least ten times in the morning, during the day and at night.

You can work with one affirmation at a time or several at the same time, whatever feels the most powerful for you.

Take your time with this, the process can be spread over a period of weeks.

Remember:

IF YOU REPEAT IT YOU KEEP IT

As you change your beliefs, so you will have noticed a change in your thoughts.
As you take control of your thoughts you will begin to notice a change in your feelings.

6.

STEP THREE:
YOUR EMOTIONS

**THE LIGHTEST OF ALL BODIES
IS ONE WHICH WAS ONCE HATED
AND IS NOW LOVED**

**IF YOU IGNORE HOW YOU FEEL
YOUR BODY WILL IGNORE YOUR ATTEMPTS
TO CHANGE HOW IT LOOKS**

GETTING IN TOUCH WITH YOUR FEELINGS

Fill in the next four pages with what makes you angry, sad, happy and fearful.

ANGER

Sadness

Happiness

Fear

WHICH ONE DO YOU FIND EASIEST TO EXPRESS?

It is likely to be the emotion most regularly expressed in your household as a child.

If there are some emotions which you feel awkward writing about, or which you do not wish to write down at all, these are probably the ones which were least often expressed in your family.

Every family has its own range of emotions which are accepted and encouraged, and other emotions that are discouraged or not permitted.

Some emotions may not have been expressed at all.

They may have all been suppressed.

Remember:

WHAT IS NOT EXPRESSED IS SUPPRESSED

One of the most popular ways of suppressing feelings is swallowing them down with food.
The degree to which you were able to identify and freely express all your emotions as a child results in your *emotional literacy* as an adult.

EMOTIONAL LITERACY

Emotional literacy is being used here as a term to describe how healthily you are in touch with your emotions, how you recognise, acknowledge, identify and express them.
Because some emotions are more acceptable in a family, a child sometimes learns to substitute the acceptable emotion for the real feeling. This process is often continued into adult life and remains below our normal level of awareness.

For example:

Instead of showing fear we might show anger.
Instead of showing anger we might show sadness.
Instead of showing sadness we might show anger.
Some people will laugh as a blanket cover for emotions.

Expressing a substitute emotion does not express what we are really feeling and so we continue to carry it around with us, storing it away somewhere in our body.

If we have not learned how to identify our feelings we are often confused as to what we are actually feeling.

IDENTIFYING YOUR EMOTIONS

To express our emotions we need first to identify what that emotion really is.

Emotions are a physical reaction to a thought.

Locating where you physically experience an emotion in your body is helpful in identifying what you are truly feeling.

It is also helpful when you want to let go of a suppressed emotion.

Going through the following process will help you locate where you physically experience an emotion.

SADNESS

Look at your list of what makes you sad. Really be with the feeling.

If necessary focus on a particular event.

Notice where in your body you are experiencing that feeling.
(If you are not able to be in touch with it immediately then give it a little time. If you still cannot find it, wait until you experience the feeling and then make a note of where it occurs in your body).
Colour it in on the picture of your emotional body.

Repeat the process with

ANGER
FEAR
HAPPINESS.

For example, some people might feel anger in the chest, sadness in the stomach, fear in the intestines and happiness all over.

We are all unique and it is not at all unusual to feel emotions in the hands, arms, legs and even the genitals.

MY EMOTIONAL BODY

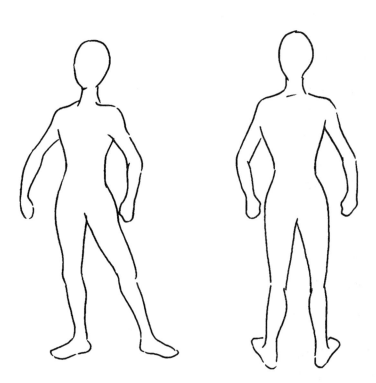

Write in and shade in where you feel your emotions

UNRESOLVED EMOTIONS

WEIGHT IS JUST THE DISGUISE
FOR WHAT IS REALLY WEIGHING HEAVILY ON YOU

Unresolved and unexpressed emotions are probably the greatest cause of over-eating. We frequently use food as a substitute for emotional expression and store the weight of those emotions in our body for years.

All negative emotions are telling us that there is a need to change. That there is a better way of experiencing life.

FINDING THE UNRESOLVED EMOTION

We are constantly trying to balance ourselves emotionally. To achieve this emotional balance we need less of those emotions we suppress and more of those emotions we feel we are lacking.
When we eat and we are not hungry we are usually entering an emotional *state*, even though we may not be aware of it.

We can call this *state-dependent eating.*

MY STATE – DEPENDENT EATING

Fill in the bubbles with your state – dependent eating

1) To give yourself some clues to the link between your emotions and food, fill in the diagram on *My state-dependent eating*. You do not need to complete all of these. If you become aware of more connections between food and emotions as you go through this chapter, then write them here.

2) Go through the following negative emotions and note anything which comes up for you.
Anything that you might call unfinished business.
Any emotion which you feel you have been suppressing.

ANGER
SADNESS
FEAR
GUILT
RESENTMENT
JEALOUSY

One way of finding these unresolved emotions is to go through your life from the earliest time you can remember, up to the present time and see what still brings a bad feeling for you.
Another way is to run through the major relationships and influential people in your life and see what comes up.

Myself
Partner
Friends
Children
Parents
Partner's parents
Boss
Work colleagues
Teacher

e.g. Anger towards father
    Fear of boss
    Sadness about partner

UNRESOLVED EMOTIONS

WHAT EMOTIONAL BAGGAGE ARE YOU STILL CARRYING?

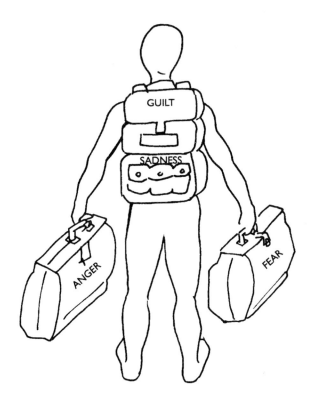

You can also grade the strength of your emotions from one as the strongest down to five as the weakest.
This will help to clarify which emotions to let go of first.
For instance, it will be more useful to let go of first degree anger before fifth degree fear.

There are degrees of emotions, for which we use many different words. These can also be a key to identifying unexpressed emotions.

ANGER:
cross
annoyed
frustrated
resentful
impatient
irritated
livid
furious

FEAR:
anxious
nervous
insecure
fearful
scared
petrified
panic
horror

SADNESS:
disappointed
hurt
sad
unhappy
discouraged
downhearted
dejected
miserable

If you are finding these exercises on feelings uncomfortable then there
is a good chance that you are already moving in the right direction.

If you are finding it difficult, or overwhelming, then get the help of a
professional counsellor or therapist to help you through. Take care of
yourself, do not try to do too much on your own.

**IT IS TRULY A JOY WHEN YOU DISCOVER
THAT YOUR HAPPINESS DOES NOT DEPEND ON YOUR
RELATIONSHIP WITH FOOD**

LETTING GO OF EMOTIONS

There are ways of working through the emotion on your own.

Here are some:

1) Identify and locate the emotion through the process above.

2) Thank the emotion.
It is serving a purpose. It is a signpost to change. However bad it feels whilst you are holding on to it, it is guiding you forward, letting you know that it is time to look at things differently.

3) Take time to be with the emotion.
Do not push it away from you or ignore it. Doing so will only reinforce the process of suppression. Experience what the emotion brings up as you take time with it and explore it. There is a great deal of truth in the saying, *"You are never upset for the reason you think you are,"* so ask yourself some questions about the feeling.

What else could this feeling be about?

What could I learn from this feeling?

Do I want to keep this feeling?

Am I hanging on to it to make somebody else feel guilty or bad?

Do I want to let this feeling go?

Who does the feeling hurt?

What do I need to start thinking to let this feeling go?

Is this feeling familiar?

Have I let go of it before?

What learning can I take forward with me this time?

4) Ask yourself: What do I need to change within myself to feel different?

This may need a change in belief from:
I am not responsible for what I feel, to: I am responsible for what I feel

It may need a change in your thoughts so that you are able to respond to a situation in a different way.

It may need a letting go of the emotion to realise and learn that it is less painful to let go of it than to hang on to it.

5) Imagine yourself changing what you need to change and how it would feel if you did.

6) Repeat this imagined change several times.
There may be a tearful or other physical release as this goes on.
It is the release of the old emotion which causes this.
The taking up of the new way of feeling is usually accompanied by a sense of relief and pleasure.
Very often we feel physically lighter the moment the old negative emotion is gone.

7) There may be some remnants of this emotion still left to come up
If you sense that there are, then repeat the process.

TRAPDOOR

When a release takes place there is very often a profound letting go of an emotion.
However, if we continue our old thought patterns and do not learn to think differently, there is a possibility that we will go through the process of creating and suppressing that emotion all over again.

Be wary!
If you sense this happening, nip it in the bud. The sooner you go through the above process, the quicker and easier it is.

LETTING GO WITH A LETTER

This can be very useful for letting go of unexpressed anger, long-term resentment, guilt, or sadness.

1) Write a letter that you are not going to post. It can sometimes be useful to have a photograph of the person you are writing to in front of you.

2) In this letter use whatever language you want to use, do not bother about being too careful how you write it. Just let it flow. Whatever wants to come, just let it come. Say exactly how you are feeling.

2) Give yourself a reward for having written the letter.

3) When you have finished put the letter away and arrange with yourself when you will next look at it. It is best to make this within the following week.

4) Next time you take it out decide how long you are going to spend with it. Read it through. If there is something there that you no longer wish to say then cross it out. If there is something more you want to say then continue writing.

5) Stop at the time you have agreed with yourself. Put the letter away again and give yourself a reward. Arrange a time you will look at the letter again.

6) Repeat this process until you can take the letter out twice and do not wish to add anything.

7) Decide what you want to do with the letter. You can make a little ritual of burning it if you wish and watch your anger or other emotion go up in smoke and blow away. Do not post it, but do whatever else you wish with it.

8) If you do not feel any different when you have completed this letter then there is still more work to do.

ANGER

Anger can take various forms. It can be expressed at the appropiate level, at the right time to the right person. Unfortunately, most of the time this does not happen.

Much anger is expressed towards partners and others who have done very little to deserve it. Misdirected anger can sometimes persist for years in a relationship, often when the anger is longstanding and really meant for a parent.

When anger is denied or suppressed it can either explode into violence or can be swallowed for years often showing itself in weight gain and also in physical disease.

Underlying simmering anger can create a bad family atmosphere and general discomfort throughout a household.

Very often our anger is based on unrealistic expectations of another person. If they do not do something we want them to, or do not do it in the way that we want it done, we choose to be angry. If we change our expectations we change our response. Try it. You will be surprised.

There are many useful, simple ways of expressing anger.

Here are a few:

1) You can talk to the person as if they were in the room with you or sitting in a chair opposite you. It is best to do this when you are alone in the house! You can really say exactly what you want to say and just how you feel. You are not going to hurt anybody with what you say, so say, or shout, exactly what you want to.

2) You can thump or pummel a cushion or a pillow, again expressing yourself vocally.

3) Think and investigate what it is costing you to suppress and hang on to that anger, physically, mentally and emotionally. No matter what payoffs or benefits you think hanging on to anger might bring, it can never be healthily held on to.

FEAR

Fear can sometimes serve a positive purpose, slowing us down and guiding us forward in the right direction.

It can also be so strong that we are immobilised and do not take any action to grow or move forward in our lives.

Although at first we do not realise it, many of us carry hidden fears about the prospect of losing weight.

Fear of success is common.

If you lose weight you will feel more attractive and you may be tempted to stray from your current relationship.

It may mean you will be more active socially and you do not know if you can handle that.

Success may mean that you will be under pressure to keep the weight off, and the pain of putting it back on would be too much to contemplate.

Success may mean that you are a threat to your parent's idea of how you should be.

There are many other fears too:

Fear of taking action
Fear of being responsible
Fear of failing
Fear of being rejected

Fear usually contains a self-limiting belief.
You do not have to look too closely before you find it.
Ask yourself what it is costing you to hold on to this fear.
What obstacles is it putting in your way?

How is it stopping you achieving what you want to achieve ?

MAKING FRIENDS WITH YOUR FEAR

Again, enlist the power of your imagination.

1) Imagine how things would be different if you let go of that fear.
How would you be different?
What opportunities would you take that you used to let pass by?
What could you achieve if you passed through that fear?

2) Repeat this process over and over again.

3) Experience the fear alongside you.
If the fear is by your side it cannot be in the future.
Seeing our fears in the future only feeds the fear and makes it stronger.

Fear and excitement create virtually exactly the same physical sensations within our bodies.
Allow the fear that is now alongside you to turn into excitement.
Allow the excitement to encourage you forward, to achieve just what it is you want to achieve.

SADNESS

Sadness is usually associated with loss. It can be a major loss in the form of a death, loss of a house, a job or a relationship. Whatever the cause, it is vital that the pain of the loss is allowed to reach the surface and express itself. Suppression of the feelings of grief are incredibly stressful and can be physically debilitating.

Experiencing the pain of loss and going through the process of grieving is essential to health. If you remove the blocks to emotional expression of sadness it will readily find its way to the surface. Rather than trying to push the emotion away it is important to stay with it and allow it to surface. If you feel you need help through this process, then do find it.

GUILT

Guilt is something which often weighs heavily upon us, but it cannot really be described as an emotion. It is rather a feeling we have that lies on top of emotions. It is a harmful and particularly useless burden to carry. Hanging onto guilt achieves nothing but pain. Guilt is always focused on an event in the past. An event which can never be changed. Guilt comes either from childhood values where you are still trying to get the approval of parents and perceive yourself as failing, or from breaking your own standards of behaviour which you have set at an unobtainable level.

If we look a little more closely at a feeling of guilt there is usually an underlying feeling of resentment. If we let go of this, the guilt itself often disappears.

One of the most effective ways of removing guilt is to examine your *shoulds*. If you are hanging on to guilt look again at the section on *shoulds* in the last chapter.

The most important thing to remember as you let go of your guilt is to forgive yourself. Whatever you did was merely an attempt to meet your needs at that time.

If you had known better at the time you would have done something differently.

WHAT ARE YOU REALLY HUNGRY FOR?

This is the most important question to ask yourself when looking at unresolved emotional issues.

Just as there are emotions which we may need to express and let go of, there are also emotions we would like to have more of in our lives.

There are some very useful things you can do to find the answer to this very important question.

Complete the following sentences without using the words thin or fat, or words which mean the same like slim, tubby etc.

1) Losing weight will make me feel more.....

2) Losing weight will make me look more.....

3) Losing weight will make me be more.....

4) Losing weight will make me feel less.....

5) Losing weight will make me look less.....

6) Losing weight will make me be less.....

The weight of our body is a reflection of an inner imbalance.
The answers to the first three questions above reflect what you want to have more of in your life.
The answers to the last three reflect what you want to have less of in your life.

WHAT ARE YOUR UNREALISTIC EXPECTATIONS OF FOOD?

When you catch yourself doing one of the following:

constantly looking for food
over-eating
automatically eating without being aware of it
eating and not being able to stop
eating when you are not hungry

Then stop for a moment and take what can be called a *diagnostic pause.*

Think for a moment what is really going on for you.

What are you expecting food to do for you?
e.g:
   I expect food to make me feel less lonely
   I expect food to take away my depression
   I expect food to take away my boredom
   I expect food to heal the pain of a relationship
   I expect food to relax me
   I expect food to...............................
   Etc...............................

There may be only one of these things or there may be several.

If you have unrealistic expectations of food it can lead to a situation where instead of looking at the real issue that concerns you, you eat, and eat, and eat!

Over-eating then becomes the problem that you focus on and the original issue falls below your level of awareness.

And so...
you suppress the need for something in your life.
Or...
you do not acknowledge what you are really hungry for.
Or sometimes both!

Once this takes place you will never successfully change your eating habits unless you address the original cause and change your unrealistic beliefs and expectations of food.

OVEREATING AND DIETING
ARE SIMPLY WAYS
OF NOT GETTING YOUR TEETH
INTO THE REAL ISSUE

WHAT DO I USE FOOD AS A SUBSTITUTE FOR?

Just as a dummy is used as a *pacifier, comforter* and *soother*, so it is sometimes the case that we use food not only as a way to suppress feelings, but also as a substitute for something we are lacking in our lives.

Do any if these sound or feel familiar for you?

I use food as a substitute for comfort
I use food as a substitute for love
I use food as a substitute for a relationship
I use food as a substitute for expressing my feelings
I use food as a substitute for company
I use food as a substitute for being held
I use food as a substitute for support
I use food as a substitute for sex
I use food as a substitute for.............(add any of your own reasons)
Etc.............

If you find that this is true for you, that you do indeed use food as a substitute (and you probably do!), then somehow you have acquired the belief that this is possible, that food could actually be used in place of something else lacking in your life. Of course this is not possible, and because it is affecting your weight, neither is it acceptable.

IF YOU FIND WHAT YOU ARE TRULY HUNGRY FOR
ALL CRAVINGS WILL DISAPPEAR

Identifying what you are really hungry for, and then bringing it into your life, allows you to stop using food as a substitute.

There is only one thing that we are all hungry for, and every label we put on our reasons for eating can be traced back to this.

It is of course **LOVE.**

We either use food as a substitute for the love we would like to receive from others, or for the love we do not give to ourselves.

Often we are mistaken by what we regard as love in a relationship. What we call love may really be a need to feel secure, to have someone to admire, to have someone take care of us, someone to be dependent on, someone to make decisions, someone to please, someone to approve of us, someone to continue the role of our parents, someone to be there, someone who will take us out of the home environment or someone who will provide for us materially.

Many of these values are what we call *ego-based* in that they are born through fear.

A relationship may hold together if two partners satisfy each other's needs and expectations, but real love can only exist in a relationship where each individual is allowed to be an individual. Where both partners can grow emotionally and spiritually. Where growth and change are welcomed as gifts, not seen as threats to the relationship.

We are only able to love others as much as we are able to love ourselves.
Some people squirm even at the thought of this.

Learning to love ourselves can seem a very strange concept, for most of us are brought up to judge, criticise, disapprove and undermine ourselves.

EXERCISES IN SELF LOVE

What would you like to do for yourself that you have been putting off for some time?

Write down a list of the things that you have been denying yourself.
e.g.
going to the hairdresser
going dancing
buying a book
buying clothes
going to the theatre
taking a day out
buying some flowers
having a holiday
asking for help with something etc.

Choose at least six.
Decide to do them.
Do them with pleasure and enjoyment.
Really treat yourself.
Allow yourself to feel really good about doing them.
Do them in a loving way.
You are a special person. You are a valuable person.
You are worth it.
Do them.

Fill in the hearts

Here is another way:

1) Take a sheet of paper and write the reasons you have for not loving yourself. Things you may not like about yourself which you think make you unloveable.
Begin each statement with the words:

I am .....

Then write them in on the bubbles around the diagram, but precede them with the words:

I love myself even when I am .....
e.g.
I love myself even when I am short-tempered
I love myself even when I am forgetful
I love myself even when I am feeling sorry for myself

Spend some time with that feeling.
Repeat these affirmations as often as you can, until you begin to notice the change in feeling.

As we learn to love ourselves, so much weight drops from our mind.

Ask yourself:
How can I be more loving to others, to my partner, to friends, children?

and **START NOW!**

MOST OF WHAT WE DO IS DONE TO DRAW LOVE INTO OUR LIVES.
IF WE DO NOT FIND LOVE,
MOST OF WHAT WE DO IS DONE TO COMPENSATE FOR THE LACK OF LOVE

7.
STEP FOUR:
YOUR BEHAVIOUR

**FROM IMBALANCE
TO IN BALANCE**

THE MOST EFFECTIVE DIET
IS ONE OF
SELF-KNOWLEDGE
SELF-ESTEEM
AND LOVE

Having discovered and let go of our underlying reasons for eating inappropriately, sometimes we are still left with an unwanted behaviour - the habit of over-eating.

Now it is time to let go of over-eating.
You do not need it any more.
Now is the time to bring over-eating into line with your new beliefs, your new thoughts and your new emotional balance.
It is no longer satisfying a need or serving a purpose.

Again, small steps can be the most effective way of permanently changing habits.

EATING HABITS

A habit is just a learned behaviour that has been repeated until it has become automatic.
It can be changed.
If you are experienced in the world of weight loss you may have picked up some good habits along the way. You have probably also found yourself hanging on to some bad habits that work against you.
List your eating habits now, one list called **HEALTHY** and one below **UNHEALTHY.**

e.g. under HEALTHY you might put
I eat a lot of fruit
I do not eat late at night
I drink enough water

under UNHEALTHY you might have
I eat too much sugar
I eat too often
I eat before I eat a meal

**IF YOU TRULY RECOGNISE THE MIRACLE OF
YOUR BODY
YOU WILL GIVE IT ONLY THE FOODS IT
WOULD CHOOSE.**

BREAKING YOUR UNWANTED HABITS

Here are a number of strategies for breaking those unwanted habits.

Look how many unwanted habits you have on your list.
Imagine if you were to successfully change one of those every week
until you had got rid of all of them.
How many weeks would that take?
When you think that you have spent a lifetime finding and using these
habits, letting go of them in a few weeks is very quick indeed.

There is a high probability that as you have worked through *Slim From
Within* that some of those unwanted habits will have already
disappeared.

The good news is that when you have dealt with the causes underlying
your over-eating, you will be able to eliminate some of those habits in
a day!

If you let go of an old habit for one day you merely need to repeat the
process the next day until you have let go of it completely.

**PEACE OF MIND
IS FAR MORE COMFORTING
THAN A PIECE OF CAKE**

CHOOSE TO CHANGE ONE HABIT AT A TIME

Do you give yourself a
mountain to climb?

when there is a much
easier way

So often people will try and change too many habits at once.
Taking on too much so that it is virtually impossible to achieve.
Every day they feel as if they have a mountain to climb and eventually they just give up.

Choosing to change one habit at a time is much more realistic.
Because it is so much more achievable, it brings great satisfaction and motivation.
It also creates a learning process that makes progressively changing your habits that much easier.

These habit changes can be very simple!

1) Start with a question.

Ask yourself this when you wake up in the morning.

WHICH ONE HABIT CAN I CHANGE TODAY TO GREATLY IMPROVE MY CHANCES OF PERMANENT WEIGHT LOSS?

Ask yourself this every morning.

AND THEN DO IT!

It may well be that for several days you choose to work with the same habit. That is the most effective way of working.

Here are some strategies to help you achieve it:

A) To interrupt an automatic behaviour pattern which has become an unwanted habit you can change one of several elements:

The time
The quantity
The speed
The place
The accompanying activity
The quality of the experience

So let's take an unwanted habit:

e.g.Eating three biscuits with a cup of coffee each morning at 11am.

1) **Change the time.** Decide you will have the biscuits one hour later if you choose.
When 12 noon comes you can choose not to have the biscuits, you have never had them at this time before, why start now? Repeat this on a daily basis and after a few days the habit is gone.

2) **Change the quantity.** Choose to have two biscuits instead of three, then one instead of two, then none at all. Set yourself a short term goal and stick to it.

3) **Change the speed.** Eat very, very slowly. It can get so boring and tedious that after a few days you may find no pleasure in it and that it is just not worth doing.

4) **Change the place.** If you are used to having your coffee and biscuits in a particular room, then do not go into that room at that time. If you really want to go into the room then the price of going in might be not having the biscuits.

5) **Change the accompanying activity.** Do not have the coffee with the biscuits. If you read a newspaper at the same time then do not do it. Changing all the associations breaks the automatic behaviour and after a few days the idea of having the coffee without the biscuits can be very attractive.

6) **Change the quality of the experience.** Buy biscuits you do not like! Make your coffee much stronger or weaker so that you do not experience the ritual in the same way. Eat an apple instead.
Above all, find an alternative behaviour which gives you satisfaction and pleasure.
You can replace the biscuits with a really good feeling of achievement. That is far more fulfilling.

Do these until you find one which works for you.

All these processes may seem small, but they raise the automatic behaviour to a conscious level. They give you an opportunity to make choices and decisions and to successfully let go of an unwanted habit.

Each unhealthy habit broken is a step in the right direction.

Remember, if you feel deprived in some way when you are breaking a habit then you are looking at things in the wrong way.

B) Ask yourself these questions,

What is the price of keeping my old habits?
What will it cost me in the short-term and the long-term if I do not change those old, unwanted habits?

Write the answers down.
Is that a price that I am willing to pay?

Now write down the rewards that will come from successfully breaking all your habits. All the pleasure and satisfaction that you will get from achieving this.

Which do you choose to have?

The pleasure of moving forward?
Or the pain of staying where you are?

REMEMBER

REPEAT IT AND YOU KEEP IT

Repeat the change and you keep the change.

When you have successfully interrupted an unwanted behaviour pattern, acknowledge it.
Compliment yourself, give yourself a reward, a gift, really feel good about it. You deserve it!

Every time you acknowledge your success with a compliment and reward, you reinforce the change.
The more you reinforce it the stronger it gets.
Your unconscious will always follow the stronger of two ideas.
This reinforcement will make the new pattern so strong that you will follow it automatically.
Your unwanted eating habit will become so weak that it will just shrivel and disappear.

PAIN OR PLEASURE

This is one of the most effective ways of habit breaking. It is all about choice.

Choice is about creating a pause between the impulse to do something and your response to the impulse.

Being experienced in the field of weight loss, you are no doubt familiar with some of your automatic eating patterns: opening the fridge door *again*, making *yet another* sandwich or taking *yet another* chocolate. Sometimes finding yourself eating without even realising you are doing it, taking something from the fridge without even giving a thought as to whether you are actually hungry or not.

Here is a way to deal with these.

1) Write on a piece of paper all the negative associations you have with being overweight. You will be very familiar with these by now! Add to your list, everything it is going to cost you not to change in terms of self-image, self-esteem, emotionally, in relationships and with regard to your health if you do not lose weight.
Put it in an envelope.
Write on the front of the envelope:

INVITATION TO PAIN

2) Write on a piece of paper all the good things that taking care of your body in a healthy positive way can bring you.
Weight loss, self-esteem, new opportunities, confidence, good self-image etc. and all the details of what feeling good about your body will bring you.
Put it in an envelope.
Write on the front of the envelope:

INVITATION TO PLEASURE

3) Now take some bright coloured card or paper. Red is a good colour for *DANGER*.
Cut it into small circles or squares about five centimetres or two inches wide and place them in those places where the old, unwanted eating habit used to begin.
e.g.
On the fridge door
On the bread bin
On the biscuit packet
etc.

If you write *Slim From Within* on them you will trigger many of the associations with new learning you have been making during the time you have spent on this course

4) Each time you see one of these and are about to eat, ask yourself:

AM I TRULY HUNGRY?
IS THIS THE FOOD I REALLY WANT RIGHT NOW?

Be honest with yourself.

If the answer is *no*, then your choice is simple, **DO NOT EAT!**

Feel good about that.

Open your ***INVITATION TO PLEASURE*** and really indulge yourself in the satisfaction of what you are doing. Let that really good feeling be a reward and congratulate yourself.

If the answer is *no,* but you choose to eat anyway, then open your ***INVITATION TO PAIN*** and see how that feels. Do not judge yourself, criticise yourself or call yourself a failure in any way. Just acknowledge the feeling that you have and know that next time you can choose **PLEASURE** instead of **PAIN.**
The choice is yours.

If you consistently choose **PAIN**, then there is something you have not acknowleged so far, somewhere in your beliefs, thoughts or emotions. Use some of the exercises in the course to look at that or enrol the help of a professional to discover what it is.

5) Take a few moments to run through this process in your imagination.
See yourself choosing not to eat if you are not genuinely hungry.
Really strengthen the feeling of taking that decision.
Let the feeling move through your whole body and notice the positive energy it gives you.
Rehearse this behaviour.
See yourself doing it again and again.

Remember:

REPEAT AND YOU KEEP IT

HOW DO I BEHAVE PHYSICALLY?

**When we truly believe we can lose weight,
When our thoughts are consistent with our belief and supportive,
When we have let go of the weight of negative emotions,
Our bodies are free to follow the pathway to permanent weight
loss.**

One way to very quickly bring our bodies into line with our beliefs,
thoughts, emotions and behaviour is to **act as if**.

Act as if you are already slim inside and the weight is falling away
from you.

Act as if your posture is that of a slim person.

Act as if your facial expressions reflect that sense of inner health and
achievement.

Try it now.
See how different you feel when you draw yourself up to your full
height.
When your stomach muscles are tight.
When your breathing is deep and calm and reflects your confidence.
Notice how you feel different when you stand this way.

Collapse back into your old posture and notice how this feels.

Now resume your new posture which reflects those new beliefs and
thoughts.

Practise it every day.
Spend your day allowing your mind and body to be in full agreement
about your decision to effectively and permanently lose weight.
Being aware of yourself physically in this way allows all your inner
resources to be accessed and used at all times.
Your body is in agreement with your internal processes.

Believe you can successfully and permanently lose weight.
Overcome your negative self-sabotaging thoughts.
Freely express your emotions.
Change your old unwanted, excessive eating habits.
Show yourself in the mirror that your body reflects these changes.
And set off on your pathway to permanent weight loss!

WHERE TO GO FROM HERE

As has been said before, you cannot arrive somewhere if you do not know where you are going.

So where do you want to go with weight loss?

GOAL SETTING

This is very simple.

Goals should be:

Clear
Positive
Realistic
Maintainable

A short-term goal is useful because it brings results which are motivating and supportive

Your short-term goal is a step on the way to permanent weight loss and will help to reinforce the new habits you are successfully choosing to have.

But if you have only a short-term goal it can work against you rather than for you.
If your goal is to lose weight for a wedding or holiday, or important social occasion, and that is the only reason you have for losing weight, then do not be surprised at what happens after the event.
You have given your unconscious a short term goal without any indication of what is to happen in the long term.
The likelihood is that the weight will return, together with old eating patterns and you will wonder what went wrong.

It is absolutely essential to have a long-term ongoing goal.

Short term goal:

I am going to lose ten pounds,
I know I can do it,
I am going to lose a pound a week,
I can keep to this target.

A long-term goal is essential to permanent weight loss.

Long term goal:

I am giving my body the freedom and support to find its
healthiest weight.
I am giving my body the food I know is best for it.
My body is losing the weight it is healthy for it to lose.
It will continue to lose it until it reaches a happy balance.

Most people attempting to lose weight do not truly believe that they can, they undermine themselves with negative self-sabotaging thoughts, they still use food to deal with an unexpressed emotion, and then they SET UNREALISTIC GOALS!

It is not surprising that they are not successful!

Here is an example of a confusing and unrealistic goal:

I want to lose about half a stone   *UNCLEAR*
I will give it a try   *IT IS OKAY IF I FAIL, ISN'T IT?*
I want to lose it in two weeks   *UNREALISTIC*
I do not need to think what happens after that   *UNMAINTAINABLE*

SET YOUR GOAL NOW!

You know what has not worked in the past so do not bother repeating it unless you truly believe it can work for you now.

When you set your goal, remember:

IF YOU INSIST ON CONTINUAL DIETING YOU HAVE A
VERY SLIM CHANCE OF BEING PERMANENTLY SLIM

Choosing to have a healthy eating plan for life is the most effective way of achieving permanent weight loss.
Setting unrealistic goals will bring you disappointment and failure.
Losing one pound a week is realistic and maintainable.
Having a long-term goal is essential.

MY SHORT-TERM GOAL
(Complete it now)

1) (CLEAR).................

2) (POSITIVE)..............

3) (REALISTIC)..............

4) (MAINTAINABLE)...............

MY LONG-TERM GOAL
(Complete it now)

1) (CLEAR).................

2) (POSITIVE)..............

3) (REALISTIC)..............

4) (MAINTAINABLE)...............

CONGRATULATIONS ON HAVING REACHED THIS PAGE!

Now is the time to consolidate all your learning and all the good work you have done on yourself.

Go through the book and underline or highlight all the new learning you have found valuable and all the positive statements you have written.

Look at them regularly.

If you find yourself having difficulty with a belief, thought or emotion, go back to the appropriate section and work through it focusing on the difficulty you have.

If you still have difficulty then get help. You will find a list of helpful addresses and telephone numbers in the back of the book.

MY AGREEMENT WITH MYSELF:

Fill this in. It will confirm your new resources and approach to weight loss and show you where you can grow even stronger.

1) What am I going to achieve?

2) How am I going to achieve it?

3) How will I and others know when I have achieved it?

4) How might I sabotage myself?

5) How will I avoid sabotage?

6) How will I celebrate achieving my short-term goal?

7) How will I celebrate achieving my long-term goal?

THE FUTURE

USE WHAT WORKS FOR YOU!

When you are adapting to your new healthy lifetime eating plan, find the way that is going to be the most effective, comfortable, enjoyable and maintainable for you.

There are many options but before taking up any weight loss programs, check out the following things for yourself,

Do I work best on my own, with a friend or in a group?
Choose the way that you will find most supportive.

Is what I am doing healthy?

Do I have a short-term and long-term goal?

To lose weight there are three simple rules:

**EAT LESS
EAT A HEALTHY BALANCED DIET
EXERCISE MORE**

That is all.
If you follow those you will lose weight.

To maintain weight loss:

**EAT A HEALTHY BALANCED DIET
EXERCISE REGULARLY**

That is all.

**THERE IS A PATHWAY WHICH IS YOURS
TREAD IT BOLDLY
TREAD IT WITH PRIDE
YOU ARE WORTH IT.**

A few suggestions for further reading :-

The Road Less Travelled	M. Scott Peck - Arrow 1983
Feel the Fear and Do It Anyway	Susan Jeffers - Century 1987
Living Magically	Gill Edwards - Piatkus 1991
Opening Our hearts To Men	Piatkus 1989
You Can Heal Your Life	Louise Hay - Eden Grove
The Power is Within You	Louise Hay - Eden Grove
Your Erroneous Zones	Dr Wayne W. Dyer - Sphere 1977
What We May Be	Pierro Ferrucci - Mandala 1990
Why I Am Afraid To Love	John Powell - Harper Collins
The Relate Guide to Better Relationships	Sarah Litvinoff - Ebury Press 1991
Diet Breaking	Mary Evans Young - Hodder & Stoughton

ADDRESSES:

Organisations which have a register of Therapists and Counsellors:

UK College of Complimentary Health Care
St Charles Hospital
Exmoor Street
London W10 6DZ
Tel 0181 964 1206

Metanoia Trust
13 North Common Road
Ealing W5 2QB
Tel 0181-579 2505

Association Of Professional Therapists
(Hypnotherapists)
57 The Spinney
North Cray
Sidcup, Kent
DA14 5NE

UK Council for Psychotherapy
Regents College
Inner Circle
Regents Park NW1 4NS
0171 487 7554

British Association of Counselling
37a Sheep Street
Rugby
Warwicks
Tel 01788 578328

National Centre for Eating Disorders
54 New Road
Esher
Surrey KT10 9NU
01372 469493

Diet Breakers
Barford St Michael
Banbury OX15 OUA
Tel 01869 337070

BEAT STRESS FROM WITHIN (£19.99p)
David Brookes
Book and 4 audio tapes.
Winner of the Gold award – Best Stress Management Product of the Year.

"At last an effective way to wage war on stress – I wholeheartedly recommend David Brookes' programme"
Sir John Harvey-Jones

This remarkable course contains yet more of David Brookes' unique and powerful strategies for bringing about personal change and reducing stress levels.

Following this course you will discover how to:

Live your life without the pressure of stress
Protect yourself against stress related illness
Relax and unwind easily and naturally
Get a good night's sleep
Feel less irritable, anxious and tense
Concentrate and make decisions
Live a healthier, happier and more fulfilling life

STOP SMOKING FROM WITHIN (£12.99p)
David Brookes
Book and 2 audio tapes

Have you tried to stop smoking in the past and failed?
Do you think you do not have enough willpower to quit?
Do you feel you should stop smoking but can't?
Do you think you will never succeed?

If you answer "yes" to any of these questions then you stand an excellent chance of success using **STOP SMOKING FROM WITHIN**.
The course came out top in a consumer test on Radio 4 - it was **more successful than chewing gum, nicotine patches and willpower!**
In a nation wide monitored trial carried out with a national newspaper there were some **inspiring success stories**.

Here is what some of the participants in the trial had to say;

"Five of my friends are fighting to get hold of my copy"
"This course was easier than anything else I have tried"
" I read the book one and a half times and by then all desire for a cigarette had gone".

These books are available from all good bookshops. If you have difficulty in obtaining them ring the telephone orderline 0181 938 3030 or send a cheque for the cost of the book plus £2 post and packing to FROM WITHIN LTD, PO BOX 146, SHREWSBURY SY3 8WA